SHOBHAA *at* SIXTY

Dear Tanya,
For my mentor, role & coach. I will miss your presence immensely as long as I am here. Every time I walk past your cube I will feel a void. Everything is not for a walk, I will miss your spirit, your positivity, your radiance. I know you will be you but maybe not every day!
For Roopali

*Every ending is disguised
as a new beginning — To
new beginnings ....*

SHOBHAA *at* SIXTY

SECRETS OF GETTING IT RIGHT
AT ANY AGE

SHOBHAA DÉ

HAY HOUSE INDIA
Australia • Canada • Hong Kong • India
South Africa • United Kingdom • United States

Hay House Publishers (India) Pvt. Ltd.
Muskaan Complex, Plot No.3, B-2 Vasant Kunj, New Delhi-110 070, India
Hay House Inc., PO Box 5100, Carlsbad, CA 92018-5100, USA
Hay House UK, Ltd., 292-B Kensal Rd., London W10 5BE, UK
Hay House Australia Pty Ltd., 18/36 Ralph St., Alexandria NSW 2015,
Australia
Hay House SA (Pty) Ltd., PO Box 990, Witkoppen 2068, South Africa
Hay House Publishing, Ltd., 17/F, One Hysan Ave., Causeway Bay,
Hong Kong
Raincoast, 9050 Shaughnessy St., Vancouver, BC V6P 6E5, Canada

Email: contact@hayhouse.co.in

Designed by Aeshna Roy at Hay House India

ISBN 9789380480497

Printed and bound at
Replika Press Pvt. Ltd.

There is a fountain of youth:
it is your mind, your talents, the creativity you bring
to your life and the lives of people you love.
When you learn to tap this source,
you will truly have defeated age.
— SOPHIA LOREN

To
the 'Sophia' in all of us,
regardless of which gender we belong to

Contents

Contents

Preface

On the eve of entering the sixth decade of my life, I confess I suffered a tiny panic attack. *Oh God! Was I really turning sixty? SIXTY?* How utterly depressing. Now, the world would look at me as an old hag. Worse, I'd look at myself as one. It wasn't a pleasant feeling, as you can well imagine, but being a pretty upbeat, positive sort of person, I immediately tried to convert that dreaded number into an advantage – and felt instantly better. In fact, so much better that I promptly decided to do a book on the subject. A book that would truthfully reflect my own optimism along with my anxieties. Which person is entirely free of vanities big and small at this sensitive age? Who is crazy enough to actively want to grow old, look unattractive, feel marginalized and useless? No one. The more I thought about it, the less depressed I felt. Sixty began to sound strangely compelling and complete. Better than forty or even fifty. And far, far better than seventy. We all have to get there someday . . . seventy, eighty, ninety . . . still counting . . . stop me, someone! And God willing, we do so in good health and spirits. That is the key really, isn't it? In today's day and age, we are all living much longer. Statistics hammer home the point that with better diets and fitness levels, human beings are enjoying an unprecedented extension to their lifespans. But,

longevity has no meaning if it is not coupled with wellness on all levels – physical, mental, emotional and spiritual. For all four levels to come together harmoniously, a lot of work needs to be done and frankly, there is just one mantra to be followed – start young. Do not wait to hit forty before you begin looking after yourself – it may be too late to reverse the damage by then. My advice? Begin with basic wellness routines before you touch twenty and then keep up with them for the rest of your life. It's not as tough as it sounds. The harder you work in your youth, the less you'll need to do when you are older. Remember, it all starts in your mind – that's where the heaviest action is located.

As I went into rewind mode and reconnected with my teenage years, it was possible to understand the ageing process more fully at multiple levels. Once I accepted my additional kilos since that svelte period and made peace with my crow's feet, I felt suddenly freed from the cage of age. It is this exhilarating flight and ensuing freedom I want to share with you.

If you ask me about my attitude to age these days, let me tell you I am feeling like a rich and ripe Brie – a cheese I'm particularly partial to. All I need is a glass of great red wine to round off the mellow mood. It's all about the vintage, my dear. I like to think mine was a particularly good year!

Cheers!

Shobhaa Dé

Acknowledgements

Here's a confession: I am terrified of my publisher, Ashok Chopra. When he asks me to write a book for him – I just write it! Simple. We have worked together on two books previously and I am happy to say, it has been a terrific experience. He does his job, I do mine. The rapport is perfect. This book came about because we both wanted it to happen. It was all about timing and I am glad it worked out so seamlessly.

The book you hold in your hand has been licked into its present shape by Aeshna Roy, who remains a phantom editor. We have never met, but our frequent and lively emails make me feel I'm communicating with an old friend. Besides, Aeshna was the one who pointed out the various 'missing links' when she read the original manuscript, and made me work doubly hard to connect up all the loose ends.

If you like the cover shot and think I'm looking glamourous, please congratulate India's ace photographer Farrokh Chothia for capturing the magical moment – he makes every woman he photographs look like a Goddess. Alex Kuruvilla who heads *Vogue* in India was gracious enough to share this image with us after I shot an exclusive spread for a special issue of *Vogue*.

Acknowledgements

How can I not acknowledge the contribution of my wonderful daughters Radhika, Avantikka, Arundhati and Anandita, who remind me on a daily basis that life is as beautiful as you think it, regardless of age.

CHAPTER 1

Simply Sixty

Age is strictly a case of mind over matter.
If you don't mind, it doesn't matter.

– Mark Twain

*W*hen I was sixteen years old, I never imagined I would someday turn sixty.

It was a near impossibility. *Sixty? That's old. Not just old, possibly dead.* Sixty as a number was not scary, mainly because it did not exist in my restless school-girl mind. People didn't turn sixty – they died! Cruel and horrible, but true. At sixteen, even twenty sounds ancient. But you know what? Sixty is not so terrible. In fact, it is . . . how shall I put it . . . almost satisfying.

In all honesty, I can't claim I was overjoyed at turning sixty on 7 January 2008. Mercifully, I wasn't depressed or defeated either.

Somehow it was comforting, and soothing, to have arrived at this stage. Senior citizen – who me? Absolutely.

I still had enough hair on my head (okay, I did need to touch up the roots once every twenty days), I still had my thirty-two original teeth in good condition, I still didn't need glasses (except to read small print in low light) and I had just accomplished a physical feat (scaled a part of the Great Wall of China without suffering cardiac arrest). When I looked at myself in the mirror that morning, I didn't shield my eyes or make a face. Sure, I could see crow's feet at the corners of my eyes, the furrows (deep!) between my brows, the dry patches around my mouth, the loose skin on my neck and the inevitable grey strands framing a face that was pretty drawn, even by my own standards – but so what? I smiled at my reflection. I actually smiled! My expression softened instantly. *Keep smiling*, I told myself. *This marks a new phase of your life. How you deal with it is entirely up to you. If you allow conventional wisdom to bog you down, the next few years will be hard. If you see yourself in a more positive light, you will feel better from within.* It was a very conscious decision. I was taking it not just for myself, but on behalf of all women my age who'd gazed at their reflections in oval mirrors and panicked. There was no room for dismay.

'Sixty,' I said firmly, 'is the new forty.' I must have been pretty convincing even to myself, for it was a liberating thought that freed me. For women, age is a nasty trap. Society judges women of a certain

vintage far more harshly than it does men. We are programmed to assess a woman's worth by her appearance, and let's not kid ourselves, a sixty-year-old woman is well past her sell-by date. In these times of youth obsession, I've heard ladies not yet twenty-five talk about their 'age-related issues'. *What issues?* I ask incredulously, and they trot them out – cellulite, dull hair, dull eyes, lack of energy, big butts and big tummies. I stare at these lovely ladies in utter disbelief. To my eyes they appear goddesses – lithe, graceful, bubbly and youthful. How can their self-image be this low? I have to remind myself that these young girls come from an entirely different space and their anxieties take up a different slot as well. In a world where super-achievers in various fields are celebrated earlier and earlier, twenty-five is the new middle age. If you let it be that.

For my generation, being twenty-five held limitless promise. It was the age when we believed we were peaking and in full bloom – most of us were married with one child. The rest were waiting to get married. It was an important age, not a depressing one. Imagine then the horror and shock of turning sixty!

My family had planned a small get-together at home the night of my birthday. I had had to cancel a party I'd meticulously planned in Pune due to a sudden, unexpected medical crisis (very minor but also very painful) just a few days prior to the big day. I had designed the invitation card myself. It was a replica of the poster of Madhuri Dixit's 'comeback' film, *Aaja Nachle*. I absolutely love dancing and singing (something most people don't know about me), so the only thing I wanted to do on my sixtieth birthday was to dance all night. Not just that, I wanted to be able to celebrate with a small group of people who meant a lot to me, apart from my immediate family. The card said it all – my face was superimposed on Madhuri's, and the text stated unabashedly, 'Sixty is the new thirty!' Excuse enough to regress, kick up my heels, let my hair down and . . . behave my age! The cheek of it all. Not even forty . . . but thirty! What was I thinking? Fun thoughts. Just fun thoughts.

The minute I found out that I'd have to cancel the much anticipated weekend in my favourite city (I feel most myself in Pune), my first reaction was to curse fate. I fretted and fumed over the lousy timing and how the stupid problem should have waited. Fortunately, I was permitted to indulge my rage and frustration by my understanding family. It was natural to feel let down, even though it was nobody's fault. My adorable doctor, Shaila Weling, was another person who assured me that I'd be just fine on the day of my birthday, but not fine enough to make it to Pune. 'Switch it around and celebrate the big day at home,' she suggested. That's exactly what we did.

Of course, it was a compromise and a pretty big one at that. Gone were plans for an elaborate Satyanarayan puja followed by a sit-down Maharashtrian feast served on banana leaves. Gone too, was

a classical musical performance lined up by my darling Gautam Rajadhyaksha and a Moroccan theme-night with shishas, fantastic food and a DJ spinning all my favourite tracks. 'Don't think about it,' my children urged, 'we can always do that later.' *Later? I was going to turn sixty just once!* I became petulant and cross as I sulked in a depressing hospital room with puke-green walls. Was God punishing me? Had I done something awful? I got my answer as I lay awake one night, staring glumly at the ceiling. *No honey, God isn't punishing you. It's a three-letter word called 'AGE'. Your body is going to protest in different ways from time to time so deal with it. If you think what you're going through is major, dear girl you have no idea what other people go through. Stop being so bloody self-indulgent. Get real. This is nothing. It's not even a hiccup. It can happen to anybody at any time. Stop feeling so sorry for yourself. The party can wait!*

That was it.

I came home after spending a drowsy New Year's Eve on the hospital bed. It was such a strange experience. Not since the age of fourteen (when I was 'allowed' by my parents to celebrate New Year's Eve with friends) had I missed even a single year of kicking up my heels and greeting the dawn amidst laughter and merry-making. Here I was with a dim night lamp glaring at me. Arundhati, my wonderful daughter who'd cut short her own New Year's Eve plans in Goa to be with me, was fast asleep on the adjoining cot. If she'd felt disappointed at not being with her friends through the festive season, she certainly hadn't shown it, not even accidentally. I looked at her tiny frame huddled under rough hospital blankets and sent up a small prayer to God for blessing me with loving children. All of them, in their own way, had made sure I felt cocooned by their affection and care. They'd thoughtfully dotted the room with reminders of home – small objects precious to me like my tiny plants and fresh flowers; familiar, everyday things I need – my bedside clock, the pillows I'm used to and my favourite fragrance. I stared at these through eyes brimming with tears and thought to myself, a little philosophically, how easy it was for those who know me best (my family) to understand that which I hold precious – simple, everyday, familiar objects that provide a sense of security and comfort. I was going to spend four, maybe five, days in this cold impersonal space. I hated every moment in it, but the sight of my personal possessions made up for the sterile efficiency that defines any hospital. My silver Ganpati (bless you, Chanda!) that accompanies me on all my travels was by my bedside as well, and looked concerned. My doctor smiled when I told her so; she is also a devout Ganesh follower and scrupulously observes each ritual and fast associated with the deity. I am certain she wasn't laughing – she understood.

Five days later, just two days before my birthday, I was ready to go home. Those five days had made me confront several home truths – I was as vulnerable as the next person, I wasn't 'superwoman'. I had felt scared and nervous being wheeled into the operation theatre.

I panicked momentarily when I knew the anaesthesia was about to kick in, and I'd go under. My children had seen fear in my eyes, perhaps for the first time ever. I wondered whether I should have, or could have, disguised it. Did that fear make them feel uneasy about their own future? Did they imagine I was going to die? *Was* I? I am almost certain every person being wheeled into the operation theatre for any surgical procedure feels exactly the same way. It is the one time you are compelled to come to terms with your own mortality. So many things can go wrong and often do. Don't we all know about minor surgeries that ended in disaster and death? These are morbid preoccupations that refuse to go away and no amount of rational thinking helps. No words are soothing enough afterwards, when you are out of the torture chamber and resting on a hospital bed. That is also the time for introspection and nostalgia. First you thank God for seeing you through the trauma, and then you thank your stars. That's exactly what I did.

Age, that dreaded three-letter word for most people, becomes yet another preoccupation. You remind yourself that you are no longer a spring chicken – your body has its limits even if your mind doesn't. While your imagination soars in that large but essentially depressing hospital room, your body sends out different signals. It tells you to slow down, take stock and review priorities. That's what mine told me but I wasn't prepared to listen. I ranted internally. *There are hundreds of exciting things I want to do. I've never been to South America. I* want to go to Rio. I want to samba with the world. I must tango in Argentina. How wonderful is the sound of 'Buenos Aires'? I want to see, eat, feel, touch and smell at least some of the amazing things I've dreamt about all these long years. Things I couldn't afford when I was young. Now that I had the money, now that I also had the time, how dare my body misbehave?

I was angry. This wasn't a part of my grand plan.

Someone said (a little wickedly), 'Perhaps you've attracted the evil eye. *Nazar lag gayi!* You must be careful. There is so much jealousy in the world. Your rivals are trying to destroy you!' I snorted and scoffed at this preposterous idea. *What utter rubbish. I didn't believe in superstition – why was this person putting such thoughts in my head?* And yet, despite my rational self dismissing the idea, I'd find myself lying awake during those interminable hospital nights wondering if it was true. *There are evil forces in the world. What if someone has cast a spell? Black magic doesn't exist, does it?* I can tell you now, it was absurd and I hated myself for the self-generated mental torture. I later blamed it on a combination of antibiotics and overall physical fragility. My younger, brasher self would never have permitted such regressive thoughts to enter my mind. But at sixty perspectives change, and sometimes you end up falling into a silly trap of your own creation.

Fortunately, I snapped out of this self-pitying phase as soon as I got home – there were pressing reminders around me that made it impossible not to. *Get off your butt and start working. You are one hundred per cent fine, so no excuses!* I'm glad my inner voice is so determined

and pushy. I 'got off my butt' within a day or so, deciding to ignore the discomfort and pain. Focusing on it was only making it worse. Instead, I attacked my work in a demonic fashion and found myself being very productive but in an unnaturally efficient, speeded up way. My children were initially amused and then alarmed. 'You might end up with an ulcer,' they half-joked, watching me furiously keying in text. 'I'd rather have an ulcer than a skipped deadline,' I said jauntily.

There was much I needed to prove to myself . . . even to others. Once again, I was falling into the trap of playing invincible. I realised taking it easy had never been an option for me. I'd laugh when well-meaning friends urged me to let go and relax. 'What for?' I'd mock. 'Remind me when I am ninety.' Well, here I was at sixty, pretending to be thirty and acting like I was ten. My husband Dilip scolded me (like he would any ten-year-old), 'Behave yourself . . . or else.' I knew what that ominous threat meant – no access to my laptop, cellphone or landline. I immediately decided to snap out of my manic routine and give relaxation a chance. That phase lasted no more than a week. But at least I felt I had given it a shot, if only to please my family.

We are all frail and fragile creatures, no matter how strenuously we fight it. Nobody likes to admit weakness. But health is not about weakness, it is about management and that process must begin when you are young – during those fragile teenage years when hormonal changes play havoc with your body, mind and soul. If you begin looking after your health early enough in life, your later years will be that much more comfortable. When I stare at myself in the mirror these days (less and less!), I send up a small prayer and recall the time I was sixteen . . . eighteen . . . twenty. I remember giving myself good advice. *Your body is all you have so look after it. This is your hair – preserve it well, for you won't be getting any replacements. This is your skin – it will age, acquire lines, crow's feet and those will eventually deepen into wrinkles. However, if you take care of it from now itself, you'll be able to delay the ageing process sufficiently. These are your teeth – if they go, new ones won't replace them. Brush them twice a day. Gargle after every meal. Dental hygiene is key. This is your body – if you neglect it, you will end up like a bag of bones or a sack of potatoes so take your pick. Exercise and tone your muscles. Moisturize your skin; keep it clean at all times. Oil your hair once a week – grandma can't be wrong. Don't forget about your eyes – postpone wearing glasses if you can and work those eye muscles as long as possible. Wear sunglasses in bright sunlight and don't leave home without sunblock.*

These simple tips have seen me through the best and worst of times, and as we go along this extended journey together I shall share more of them. Hopefully you will discover for yourself that living life beautifully is not difficult at all. On the contrary, awareness of all that life promises is what enhances its quality. This is what I

tell myself each morning. I frequently write 'Life is beautiful. Live it beautifully!' in the autograph books of young students. I truly believe this. It is up to each one of us to figure out that which matters most in life. If a woman is asked this question, she may reply, 'family'. A man may say, 'success'. When you put both together, it adds up to 'security'. An insecure person is an unhappy person and it shows. We are all insecure about different things – how well we contain our insecurities decides how well-adjusted we are.

I often wonder what part the appreciation of beauty (in all its incredible forms) plays in our everyday life. How sensitized are you to recognizing the myriad gifts on offer that come without a price tag? I was fortunate enough to discover my priorities early on, and live by a very basic set of rules I made for myself. This is something I urge you to do as well. No matter what your age, sit down and list out what according to you makes you happy, blisteringly happy. This is not as easy as it sounds. My list changes from time to time, but there are a few constants on it – the sound of gurgling water, the smell of babies, the taste of fresh tamarind, the sight of shell-pink sunsets and the touch of a loved one. It's a pretty long list actually, and I love rewriting it periodically. Even that act makes me happy. Simple, uncomplicated stuff, but somehow everything on the list touches my heart in a marvellous way.

The second exercise is tougher. Ask yourself, 'Who am I?' Do you really know who you are? Sometimes I do and sometimes I don't.

Sometimes I feel clever and sensitive, at other times dumb and mean – all components that make up the person called 'me'. Do undertake this task as an important exercise to discipline both your mind and your actions. For example, I know most of my strengths (I like to think I am practical, forthright and fair) but more importantly, I know my weaknesses – I took the trouble to list them out and address each one. Not that I have conquered all or even most of them, but at least I'm not running away from dealing with the stubborn ones. I know I can be impatient, abrupt and short on the fuse, but knowing that and acting on it are two different stories! Once I saw my weaknesses written down in my own handwriting, it made them more real and somehow it also made it easier to rectify them. These days, when I see the old impatience rising up, that list floats in front of my eyes and temporarily distracts me from snapping. That's good enough. The moment passes . . . I take a few deep breaths, sometimes I count to ten and save myself (plus the recipient of a sharp remark) from potential unpleasantness. I encouraged my children when they were teenagers to make similar lists. I also told them about the power of positive thinking. If you start a new project on a negative note and convince yourself it's going to fail – guess what? It is going to fail!

The other day I found myself on a boat headed for Alibag, where we have a weekend home. The lady seated to my left was young, educated and articulate. She was accompanied by two teenage children. We got talking, and she too mentioned the power of

positive thinking (were we on the same wavelength or reading the same self-help book?) when it came to one's offspring. We both laughed in motherly recognition of the trials of dealing with teen rebellion. 'I make my children write down the following lines once every fortnight, "I am a good person. I have good thoughts. I love the world and the world loves me."' she told me. I asked her if it worked. 'Oh yes,' she replied enthusiastically, 'the more they write those simple lines, the better their conduct!' Wow! I was impressed. I'd tried and failed to convince my own kids to write lines like these in the past. However, when I got home I told one of my daughters to try it. 'Do it for me,' I said shamelessly, using that old mummy trick which invariably works. She did oblige and I was delighted. She smiled brightly and said, 'I did it for you . . . but please don't ask me to do it again. It's dumb and cheesy!' Perhaps it is. Okay, I won't ever ask you to do it again. Whatever works for you, darling!

CHAPTER 2

The Spirit and Spirituality

The years teach much which the days never knew.

– Ralph Waldo Emerson

I have to admit I was never a religious person – religious as in believing there is an all-seeing, all-knowing force keeping a detailed report card on all our lives – but I like my daily rituals. I strongly believe in the power of prayer, and I pray selfishly when I need something. Terrible admission, but it is the truth.

My prayers were always need-driven, especially during my school days. My pleas to the almighty rarely went beyond 'God, please don't let me fail my physics paper!' or 'God, I really, really want to win that cup – make me win it.' I was always demanding something and giving back nothing in return. That's youth for you;

foolish, self-absorbed youth. You always think of yourself first – your priorities and your wants. I guess that's what makes God a really cool guy – he understands! He has never been unkind to me. Today, I thank him daily just for the peace and comfort that prayer gives me. My prayer is absurdly short and simple on most days. I say, '*Hey deva parmeshwara, daya kar.*' I ask for compassion. That's for starters. Then I slyly throw in a demand or two. I tell myself that it's okay – if I can't be shameless and self-seeking with God, then who else can I be that with? Predominantly though, what I feel is a deep sense of gratitude for what I have received, and not just from God, but from all those I value in my life like my immediate family, of course, but as importantly, that vast, extended family of friends and readers. Sometimes, I look into a pair of trusting eyes . . . and I see God in them. It's a great moment and an uplifting one, startling and moving in a miraculous way. These days, I sincerely attempt to set time aside for prayer in a more disciplined way, though I can and do pray anywhere, at any time. I love places of worship – from the Golden Temple in Amritsar to the Notre-Dame Cathedral in Paris. I have prayed in temples, mosques and synagogues across the world. The place doesn't matter, prayer does.

Some years back, I received a simple *mala* (prayer beads) crafted using uneven wooden beads. I started hesitantly, not knowing what exactly I was supposed to do with it. Chant the names of Gods I'm familiar with? Repeat the Gayatri Mantra? Think and utter nothing, move the beads slowly and keep my mind a blank? I decided to ask the person who'd given me the *mala* (it's from Amarnath). She said simply, 'Stand still and concentrate. Close your eyes, and repeat a simple line or two that has some meaning for you. It could be Ganpati's name. With each bead you move, say "thank you". When you finish all hundred and eight, you can either begin again, or place the beads in their usual place, light a diya, fold your hands, experience stillness, bow your head and that's it.'

I tried it the very next morning after my bath, and a strange peace enveloped my entire being for those brief minutes. The moment I bowed my head, I felt a wave of humility wash over me. It was a liberating feeling, which provided the perfect perspective. I realized I was nothing and nobody – just another tiny speck in the cosmos. What was my life really worth? Very little or a lot, depending on the importance I gave it. What is my contribution to the world? Insignificant, but I can keep trying. Where does ego come into this? It doesn't. We rarely step back and see ourselves from a distance. We rarely pause or get off that wretched treadmill. We keep going, going, going . . . somewhere or nowhere. We are too afraid to stop. And that was the revelation after I said my first *mala* in a meaningful manner – it has since become an important part of my daily life. Those few minutes spent at a small altar in my bedroom that features Gods from every religious denomination makes me aware of the vastness that exists outside me. It makes me think of how precious and fragile

each breath I take is. That consciousness has made me value life far more than anything else. It has distilled all the profound thoughts recorded by great religious leaders and philosophers down the centuries into something soothing, simple, calming and infinitely reassuring. I am thankful to the beautiful lady who gave me such an inspiring gift.

No matter what your religious beliefs are, or even if you happen to be irreligious, there is nothing wrong with investing a few minutes of your time every day just experiencing a bit of peace, getting in touch with neglected areas of your life and giving thanks for all that you're blessed with. People say the simple acts of lighting a lamp, ringing a small bell or spreading fragrance with agarbattis are ways of generating the right ambience in your environment. It certainly works for me.

I recall visiting a friend's home nearly twenty years ago, and commenting on how wonderful I felt walking into the plush living room – was it the aroma candles? The soft music? The aesthetic decor? The hostess laughed and said, 'Maybe it's the sandalwood joss sticks I light just before my husband gets back. I know how stressful his working days are. I know he likes getting home to a place that is like a haven for him, where he feels loved, understood and comforted. I make sure the lights are kept low, and believe me, I can tell from his body language and the instant change in his expression that he is happy to be here.' It sounded so very loving, easy to implement and sincere that I wondered why more of us didn't do it. Not necessarily for tired husbands, but even for ourselves? Or for those who share our lives – whosoever they are? I decided to put my friend's simple plan into motion the very next evening. Strangely, her strategy brought back memories of my own mother, who used to wait for sundown and then rush to the altar in the kitchen to light a lamp. The aroma of pure ghee burning slowly, the camphor that would serve a dual purpose (it also keeps mosquitoes away besides being used for the *aarti* or prayer), and the garlands of fresh hibiscus that added their own sweet, clingy fragrance, would greet my father and all of us when we trooped home. Why had I not followed that tradition all these years?

Well, after my friend's little lecture on modern day de-stressing tricks for hubbies on the move, I introduced something similar at my own home – it worked! If you prefer aroma candles or oils (like my daughters do), that's a good enough substitute. We live in times that require these delicate touches more than ever. We are dealing with daily anxieties and demands on our emotional and physical reserves that did not exist earlier. Why not indulge in something that's calming and appealing at the end of a gruelling day? For some it may be a glass of wine, for others music, and for still others chants, joss sticks, fresh *mogra* (jasmine flowers) and more.

Ah, *mogras* remind me of the therapeutic value of house plants. Not all of us are lucky enough to live in homes that come with lush gardens but that shouldn't stop us from planting a few seeds and watching them grow on a window sill or a small balcony. It is most enriching to track the progress of a sapling, for example, especially if you know that one day you'll wake up and see a gorgeous flower in full bloom. For that to happen, the sapling has to be nurtured, not just by changing the soil and watering it regularly or even talking to it – what works is love, genuine love. If you feel for your plant and think of it as a living presence sensitive to your voice and touch, it will respond accordingly. I love my little garden – there aren't too many plants in it, but those that are there give me so much joy. They are like my babies; each time I water them I can sense their response and know that their well-being reflects my own.

Plants, like pets, are a huge responsibility; never take them for granted. As you grow older, you'll have more time on your hands to appreciate their beauty and their moods too. We all know that pets have moods – they are practically human, remember? But plants? I am convinced plants also go through mood swings, and often I feel their moods reflect my own state of mind. If this sounds a little weird it's alright – how dull would life be without such eccentricities? A droopy plant actually tells us that it is being neglected and feeling unloved. Perhaps it needs some sunshine or a change of diet. If you tune in to your plants, you'll recognize the signs yourself. Nursing a sick plant back to life can give you immense satisfaction. I feel positively triumphant when a sad, sickly plant finally perks up after days of sulking. I find the entire nurturing process immensely therapeutic. Try it!

This goes for pets as well, as any devoted pet-lover will tell you. I always imagined I would keep a cat if I had to adopt a pet. Cats were more like me – independent and proud. They didn't need cuddling, nor did their owners have to look after them the way they had to look after dogs. Cats fed and cleaned themselves, had their own schedules, came and left as they chose but registered their presence strongly nevertheless. Yet, when the kids decided the family was incomplete without a pet, we voted for a pup! No regrets. The dogs I have known have demonstrated over and over again what noble creatures they are. When we humans talk about unconditional love we really don't know what we're saying. One has to experience unconditional love from the world's most eloquent creatures – dogs! Mute as they are, if you learn their language you will discover amazing truths about life, yourself and about them. More so if you are fortunate enough to get the chance to nurse a sick dog, which by now I have done many times. While it is an acutely draining experience, it can also be a highly rewarding one.

A sick dog is even more helpless than a sick child. At least a sick child can convey his or her discomfort, even through tears of pain and cries for help. What can the poor sick dog do but look imploringly at you and lie there, unable to even wag its tail? It is a heartbreaking sight. You feel helpless, frustrated and angry because you want to help and comfort your pet, relieve him of the agony, and yet you know he will continue to suffer in silence, unable to articulate what is bothering him. It is those moments of anxiety spent cradling a pet in your arms through an endless night that teach you about attachment, dependence, loyalty and love. Your hearts start beating as one, and each breath the suffering dog strains to take becomes your own. It teaches you compassion at its purest.

Then there are other more joyous moments when a pet steals your heart in unexpected ways and takes you by surprise – like when you are low yourself, or in tears. The house is empty; the other family members are all away, leaving you alone with your thoughts and preoccupations. You believe you are alone and free to cry in peace and privacy (women rarely get to do that). You shut the door of your room, lie down on the bed and start sobbing – sometimes for no apparent reason! Suddenly you hear an urgent scratching on the door, accompanied by whining. 'Go away,' you manage to say between sobs, but your pet isn't about to leave. The scratching at the door gets more insistent, and the whining louder. Your resistance breaks as you open the door and let the pet in. It's a decision you rarely regret. The dog doesn't ask silly questions like 'What's wrong? Why are you crying?' He just snuggles up, licks away your tears and wags his tail vigorously as if to say, 'It's okay, I understand.' Dogs work miracles. The only confidante worth trusting in the world is your pet. You can tell him whatever you want. Your deepest, darkest secrets will remain safe. What's more, there'll be no judgement call such as, 'Oh my god! How could you do that? I'm shocked, hurt and disappointed.' Too bad . . . the pet doesn't feel the same, and I'd rather believe the pet.

CHAPTER 3

The Basics

Lessons I Learnt as a Teenager about Investing in Myself

How old would you be
if you didn't know how old you were?

– Satchel Paige

*P*erhaps it had to do with the fact that I started modelling at an early age – I was only seventeen. Even though modelling in those days was not as organized or demanding as it is today (what is 'size zero' anyway?), it still required a certain level of discipline. I watched my weight, exercised in moderation, kept my face scrupulously clean, made sure my hair was oiled at least once a week and most importantly, I ate smart. This is the basic routine I have adhered to over the years, give or take a few changes based on the body's altered requirements.

LOOK AFTER YOUR SKIN

You are born with a particular skin type. The first thing to do is identify what that type is – dry, oily or combination. How does one recognize the different categories? Well, I knew mine was dry – it *felt* dry, and by the end of the day it looked dry. It helps if you listen to what your skin says – mine definitely speaks to me. It tells me clearly, 'I am thirsty. Please hydrate me.' This can happen five times a day, especially if I'm in an air-conditioned environment for hours at a stretch. If there is one beauty secret worth passing on, it is this – moisturize, moisturize, moisturize. Everyone's skin responds in a unique way to what you apply on it. I discovered mine was happiest with kitchen cosmetics. In my parents' home I couldn't afford pricey complexion-care creams so I devised my own! I started with *malai* (fresh cream) and added a few drops of lime, a spoonful of honey, plus a pinch of haldi (turmeric) to the mixture. I'd apply this on my face before showering. This became my daily routine, and it's the one routine I never gave up. Today, I may substitute the fresh cream with yoghurt, but the original formula stays.

I keep telling my daughters that good maintenance must start early in life. Don't wait till you turn forty and wake up one fine day, stare at yourself in the mirror and ask, 'Oh my God! Who's this wreck? What happened? Look at my skin, my hair, my body! What now?' It is important to understand that the 'ageing process' (how I hate that term) begins in the late twenties (twenty-seven to be precise, according to latest medical studies). I'd say it is a smart move to begin the awareness programme while still in your teens. Hormonal changes at puberty signal several important adjustments required of a woman, both emotional and physical. Unfortunately, most of us ignore these changes till it's too late.

Since my adolescence was marked by competitive sport (athletics, basketball and hockey), exercise became a part of my daily life. I was very active, toned and fit. This is an important foundation that sustains you in later life. Tuning in to your body, getting these muscles to perform and making sure to keep the stamina levels high is key to a healthier middle-age.

Because I burned so many calories per day, my mother ensured I was well fed with a nutritionally strong but simple Maharashtrian diet. I was lucky that daily diet was non-oily, light and delicious. Eggs, milk and dairy products (like cheese, yoghurt, even butter and ghee) were an essential part of my intake, along with dal, bajra rotis, chapattis, green leafy vegetables like spinach, and a small portion of rice (preferably unpolished).

These days I follow pretty much the same diet. My focus is still on high-fibre, low-fat food. Mercifully, I have never had a sweet tooth so desserts are out for me. Even as a child I couldn't get through a piece of my own birthday cake! I saved my calories for snacks I enjoyed, mainly savouries that weren't deep-fried. Today, I try and reserve my weekly treats to a glass of champagne or white wine (strictly no spirits). These treats are erratic; I may go for weeks without either or I may consume six or more glasses a week. But I do keep a tally, and rarely exceed the limit I've set for myself.

It's important not to entirely deprive the body of goodies that hit the right spot. My youngest daughter is an exercise fiend who sets impossibly high targets for herself. I am astonished by her self-control and strict adherence to dietary restrictions that I know are hard for her, since she has a sweet tooth. Instead of depriving herself totally of even a bite or two of her favourite dessert, I encourage her to work on a reward system, where she earns her tiny portion of cheesecake. Incentives always work better than harsh punishments. If you starve yourself, you end up feeling crotchety and your focus wavers. I find that used to happen to me as a student especially during my exams, when I'd forget to eat or be too tense to do so. I'd get light-headed after a few hours, depending on how my blood-sugar levels were behaving. I have since started keeping squares of dark chocolate in my handbag, but what works even faster are a couple of dates, which boost energy levels almost miraculously.

AVOID IMPOSSIBLY DEMANDING DIETS AT ALL COSTS

Crazy diets play havoc with your system. My children keep coming up with the latest 'breakthrough' plans which are connected to blood types or depend on specific food combinations (no carbs, high protein), etc. My theory regarding diets is more old-fashioned

and straightforward – the only ones that work are those you can sustain. Generally, it involves comfort foods you associate with your childhood. Work out something that isn't too elaborate, and stick to the basics. We all know steamed food is less evil than anything out of a frying pan. We also know that grilled lean meats keep the kilos away far better than fatty sausages, so why be silly about it? There is really no excuse for poor food choices in these days of information overload. Eating smart involves a lifestyle change only for those who wait till it's too late and then find it difficult to stick to the new way of eating. My advice is that you educate yourself and your children, and create a workable diet for the whole family. Leave enough flexibility in the plan so as not to frustrate those who may be less fanatical about it than you. It is important to involve the whole family in this effort, unless you want to complicate your life with three or four entirely different menus for each meal. Once you convince the people in your life about eating smart and living smart, the rest is easy. Here are a few easy-to-implement tips:

• Go easy on the salt. Teach your kids to not add extra salt to their food.

• Go easy on the sugar. Your palate gets used to a less sugary taste if you train it early enough.

• Shun deep-fried snacks, especially those deceptive ones that look very light but are lethal when it comes to the calories like *chivda*, sev, golgappas, dahi-vadas, bhelpuri, *chaklis*, *khakras*, nachos, tacos, potato-chips and similar munchies that really are hard to resist but must be energetically resisted nevertheless.

• Avoid mithai and sweetmeats. We Indians love our laddus. Basically, we love any food that is gooey, sweet, fried and rich – what can possibly compete with jalebis? Who can say no to a jalebi without accompanying sorrow? What about jalebis with a dollop of *malai*, or a blob of vanilla ice cream? God! You know how difficult it is to stop after popping one jalebi into your mouth. Ten jalebis later, you feel wretched about yourself but nothing can remove those jalebis from your system. Moral of the story? Mark off a 'Jalebi Day' in your calendar if you really crave them. Indulge yourself that day and then abstain scrupulously for the rest of the month. The same rule applies to anything else you salivate over. Blueberry cheesecake? Chocolate fondant? *Rabdi* and rasgullas (perhaps together)? Think of your weighing scale and obtain a restraining order from your brain.

• Pare down portions. Here's a candid confession. I can easily and comfortably consume up to ten chapattis at a go if the accompanying dal, vegetables and mutton/chicken curry are yummy. But do I do that? Never. I have set a quota for myself and I stick to it. My limit is two chapattis per meal, no matter how hungry I am or how greedy I feel. After enjoying these, I tell myself sternly to put the brakes on. I rarely break this rule and I do believe it isn't that hard to achieve either. Two chapattis are substantial for an adult's

appetite and it's good to follow a quota system – that applies to rice portions as well. I noticed the day I switched my attention to the vegetables on my plate and concentrated on eating those that my craving for that chapatti or bread reduced automatically. I left the table feeling full but not stuffed. I follow the same discipline with other food categories too. If I feel like eating an ice cream after a spicy meal, I make sure I sample it just to satisfy the brief craving. After a couple of spoonfuls (teaspoon not tablespoon, please note) I determinedly push the plate away. The other trick is to distract yourself by not thinking of food. Easier said than done, but if you make a conscious effort to keep your mind off your cravings by engaging it with something else (music, dance, movies, books) it generally works. For me, the visual stimulus provided by well-presented food is another huge temptation. If I can successfully avert my eyes from a fabulous spread on a buffet table, I don't feel all that bad foregoing the goodies displayed. However, if I stroll past the attractive dishes I can't resist picking up a portion ('It's okay . . . it's quite tiny!'). All those 'tiny' portions add up to one gigantic glob at the end of the meal! How will you ever knock that off? Don't believe a word of what gluttons tell you about doing an extra hour on the treadmill to sweat off the added calories – that's not how it works. Whatever you put into your body gets processed and absorbed. It's better to just eat right. It also doesn't help to skip the next meal in order to balance an earlier pigging-out session. Psychologically, you may feel virtuous at sacrificing a meal, but physically that hardly makes a difference.

• Don't follow someone else's diet. Everyone's metabolism is different. You have to first get to know your body before you embark on a diet. You must recognize the food categories that suit you. Your best friend may tell you she exists on a three-litres-of-water-and-a-banana diet. Well, good for her. Should you be following suit? Never. Your body is unique, just as hers is. You should stick to what you are comfortable with. Know your body type and metabolism. This is something you'll discover as you go along, through trial and error. Everyone tells me it is bad to eat a heavy meal after 7 PM but all my life I have eaten just one big meal a day, and that's dinner. I actively look forward to my dinner, and eat it fairly late (between 9:30 PM and 10 PM). Dieticians would throw a fit about this but it hasn't harmed me, and I cannot change my body rhythm now. My breakfast is very light (one toast, black tea, five soaked almonds and half a glass of vegetable juice). My lunch is a family joke (lassi on the run or a bowl of salad, if that), so it is dinner I look forward to the entire day. Dinner means family time. It is when I am most relaxed, the day's work done. I hate rushing through a meal, so dinners are leisurely affairs extending to forty-five minutes and more. We chat, laugh, gossip and tuck in! Someone told me to chew each mouthful as slowly as possible. I try and do that. It's a good tip. When you concentrate on chewing, you eat less. Promise! It's good for digestion as well.

• Drink hot water and green tea. I can't vouch for it, but my daughters insist it works! They drink mugs of green tea with their meals and refer to it as Chinese water torture! According to them, the Chinese and Japanese have drunk green tea for centuries and look at how healthy they are – low incidence of heart disease, etc. I don't know whether there is any scientific evidence to prove this theory. All I can say is my daughters have great skin, their eyes shine and they don't put on weight easily. I have still to try it in a serious way. I avoid drinking water with my meals. Conversely, I forget to drink water during the day, which is the worst thing for the body, especially in a climate like ours where one can get dehydrated quickly. The girls tell me I should keep a water bottle in front of me at all times as a reminder. I've tried that too – I stare at it blankly for a minute or so, tell myself it would be a good idea to drink a glass and then get back to writing, glass untouched. Don't be careless and foolish like me, go drink that water. It's good for you.

EXCERCISE!

In this city of size-zero-obsessed women, I must be among a really small minority of those who do not have a personal trainer or membership to a gym. I don't do weight-training nor do I have a treadmill at home. No personal trainer shows up to get my abs into an enviable six-pack condition. For my age, I consider myself fit enough and toned enough. The trick is to keep your goals realistic and achievable. Do not pit yourself against a twenty-year-old model or even a forty-year-old Ms Perfect Pecs. Take a good, hard look at your priorities before you look at your body's imperfections. Does your life suggest that you be an unusually attractive physical specimen with enviable proportions? In other words – are you in showbiz? Are you a TV star, a movie star, a dancer, a stage artiste or a sports person? If you don't belong to any of these categories you are not obliged to conform to any such standards or body prototypes. If you do belong to any of these vocations, then it's a part of your professional commitment to look the role. Your livelihood is directly linked to your appearance and you must respect your vocational obligations. For the rest, a reasonably well-proportioned figure ought to be enough. When I see fifty-year-old ladies with unhappy pinched faces, squeezing themselves into skintight teenage gear, I feel like walking up to them and saying, 'Relax, it's okay to have a thirty-inch waist or forty-inch hips. We would all love to be as slender as Priyanka Chopra but she is in her twenties!' Most of these women literally starve their bodies and subsist on punishing diets. The rest of the time is taken up by strenuous workout regimes at gyms. There is also the taskmaster of a trainer (the coolest status symbol to possess these days). This person dictates exactly how many grams of carbohydrates you can consume and when. Plus, your body is put

through paces that even a gymnast would find hard to match. How good does this level of torture make a woman feel? I have no idea but going by the scowls, I'd say that gaunt face on top of a rake-thin body tells its own story! And that story doesn't have a happy ending.

My own attitude towards exercise is pretty relaxed. There was a time I enjoyed brisk walks but my knees started to protest after I turned fifty. I listened to my knees. With walking no longer an option, I devised my own exercise plan that took me right back to physical education classes at school; allow me to share it with you. Before that, may I recommend swimming as a great workout that is also most relaxing? Those of you with easy access to a pool should swim at least twenty laps a day, all year round, and that ought to take care of your fitness requirements. I have my simple daily plan that I try my best to stick to but – and this is an important 'but' – on days when I have to rush to the airport or am otherwise pushed for time, I simply skip the routine and refuse to feel guilty about it. I'd noticed that I got extremely stressed out and angry if I skipped it in the past and had realized the stress was doing me more harm than what my body would've gained from the workout. I decided not to let missed sessions on holidays or weekends get to me. Frankly, it hasn't made the slightest difference to my figure – but it has certainly made me a calmer person.

The routine is very simple. I start with basic stretches to warm up the muscles. These are done standing up, legs apart and at a leisurely pace. The stretches involve toe-touching, sideways stretches and forward bends, all with regulated breathing. I also do a few specifically for the stomach muscles. These take between five to seven minutes in all. I used to do the Surya Namaskar (a yogic salutation to the sun which consists of a series of postures) but gave it up for the same reason I abandoned walking – my knees objected. If you don't have that problem, I think there is nothing like a Surya Namaskar to work out every area of the body. A set of ten complete cycles is sufficient to get the body going. You can gradually build it up to twenty cycles once your muscles get used to it. Experts consider the ancient Surya Namaskar exercise regime to be the most complete form of fitness. In case you are wondering what it involves, just look it up over the Internet, but do consult your physician before trying the routine on your own. I then do some floor exercises that include simple yoga asanas and stretches. Ten minutes is all I invest in finishing them, before ending my regime with another toe-touching set.

I have no idea whether or not this is the ideal way to keep my body fit, but so far it has worked for me. Since I spend nearly eight hours a day hunched over my desk writing, it is very important to relax my neck and shoulder muscles. They do tend to get stiff frequently, and I have suffered from a frozen shoulder several times. Neck and shoulder exercises can be done anytime, anywhere. I do them on flights or in the car. I also do them during the short breaks I take while writing. If nothing helps, I seek comfort via an old-fashioned

hot-water bottle, especially at the end of the day. That combined with a hot shower generally works, and I find my entire body gradually relaxing. Oh, how can I possibly forget the Sunday massage ably given by Babita, the lady with magic fingers? She is the only one who can unknot the taut muscles near the shoulder blades with just a little kneading. I owe her big time.

I have also taught myself to administer a firm foot massage – it is my own version of reflexology! Once you discover the pressure points on the soles of your feet, you can start pressing them gently and then increase the pressure to suit your tolerance level. You can also use a foot massager (wood, preferably) which is like a roller. One thing that works, especially before bed time, is a soothing mint-based foot cream or a foot spray. I spend lavishly on both. Mint adds softness and fragrance to the feet. Mentholated creams are divine too. Whenever friends ask me what I want from abroad, I greedily ask for foot creams, massage oils and vitamin-E-rich night creams for the face. These are my small indulgences. My friends, bless them, always oblige. For some reason, we all tend to neglect our feet and take them for granted. Considering the poor feet bear our weight all day, they definitely deserve a little pampering at night. Dry scaly skin that cracks the heel not only looks most unattractive but can lead to a painful condition if left unaddressed.

If you can afford the luxury of a long soak in a bath tub, with an array of bath salts to choose from, nothing like it. I prefer bath oils myself. These days, the market is full of locally made bath products which although expensive are entirely delightful. Fatigue is easily taken care of with just ten minutes of lying still in a tub filled with tepid water. I love aroma candles, low lighting (if any), soothing music (Chopin or Buddha Bar), fluffy towels, an invigorating back scrub and rose petals floating over the bath water. It makes me feel like Cleopatra! I don't do it all that often, unfortunately, but when I do indulge myself I feel reborn.

Before I forget – don't overlook your ears. The Chinese believe a lot can happen to make you feel better if you know your earlobes more intimately! Most traditional acupressure therapists will say the same. So will acupuncturists as they focus their needles mainly on the earlobes, the palms and the soles of the feet as there are highly sensitive nerve-endings located just there. Whatever the reason, try holding warm water in the palms of your hands and then cupping your ears for a few seconds, keeping your eyes shut. Don't ask me how it works, but it does! Do this four or five times and see the difference it makes to your energy levels.

CHAPTER 4

The Body Beautiful

When it comes to staying young,
a mind-lift beats a face-lift any day.

– Marty Bucella

With age comes ageing. There's no getting away from it. It's a self-defeating exercise to try and delay the process or go into denial about the inevitable. The body is a delicate machine and can have breakdowns. Face that fact squarely. Your body at forty, fifty or sixty and beyond is not the same body you took for granted in your twenties and thirties. Be realistic about what your body can and cannot achieve, no matter how fit you think you are. The degenerative process has begun – your bones will be more porous and your muscles lax. Your skin will lose its glow and your hair may fall to an extent that is alarming. So what?

The idea is not to give up, but to *safeguard*. Be aware that there may be activities that slow you down or weights you can no longer carry. I have stopped pulling or pushing baggage around at airports, I simply cannot do it any longer. I spend that extra money on getting a porter – believe me, it's a small investment but well worth it. It's always better to spend on a service than check into a clinic in a strange destination, without medical insurance to protect you from killer costs. Pay the bellboy well and you won't be forced to drag those gigantic bags to the elevator. I realized ten years ago that even though my arms look toned and I still have biceps, I can't really carry anything heavier than two kilos with my right hand – not even a laden dinner plate, which is why I avoid parties where I know it will be buffet-style service with little or no seating. First of all, the very thought of queuing up for food is depressing enough, and then to stand around with an impossibly heavy handbag dangling from one's free arm is just too much effort. Often, the food is not even worth the trouble! I usually eat a snack before leaving for a party (brunches are the worst!) and this way I can control my food preference and intake, or forego an uncomfortable meal altogether.

Knees, shoulders, neck muscles, spine, ankles and hip joints – pretty much the entire skeletal system – start taking their toll on your general health by the time you hit forty. Taking supplements like calcium and vitamins must be done under medical supervision as there are theories galore about how the body assimilates this

cocktail of supplements. With a certain amount of scepticism I read a brand-new survey which throws up a brand-new theory on the effects of extra vitamins, every two years. I have always been faithful to my multivitamin capsules – I take my vitamins seriously. These include vitamin E and calcium. When my resistance is particularly low, I pop vitamin B+ as a booster. This happens during travel, post-travel and on those rare days when my energy levels drop or I'm suffering from mouth ulcers. I try and avoid antibiotics completely if possible (we tend to over-prescribe antibiotics in India). Of course, when my doctor insists on them I follow the course scrupulously and always remember to neutralize the after-effects of the antibiotics with vitamin B complex.

Walking briskly is a great exercise – for those who can do it. I used to be an enthusiastic walker myself till my knees creaked and my ankles gave up. Walking had to be reluctantly abandoned. Swimming was never an option. This left me with very little to do by way of exercise, which I am a great believer in. My father never skipped his daily walk even well into his nineties. Come rain, hail or strong sunshine, each evening at precisely 6:30 PM he set off for a stroll, walking as briskly as his body would allow him to. I would be regularly scolded for not making the effort to join him. He'd dub me 'lazy'. Another well-meaning health fanatic suggested I get a treadmill. 'It takes up very little space and you can use it whenever you happen to be free, at your own time in your own space. You can read a book, listen to music or just dream.' I thought about it and decided that I didn't have the patience for such a monotonous and boring activity. No walking. No swimming. No gym. No golf. No tennis. No nothing. Like I said, it's a combination of controlled eating and basic callisthenics that has worked for me. Let me repeat this: start young! Make it a lifelong pattern. Don't expect results if you exercise in bursts.

BURNOUTS

Most women I've talked to complain of early burnouts. They give up on exercise and diets before giving themselves a fair chance to see results. It is a mental thing – one has to have the resolve in place before attempting a sustainable fitness model. A lady from the neighbourhood has been walking determinedly on the jogging track downstairs for decades. She has neither lost the extra inches nor the kilos. I watch her from my balcony whenever I'm taking a sunset break and wonder where she's going wrong. How come she has not managed to lose even a centimetre after so many years of arduous effort? Finally, I ran into her in the lobby of our building. She looked despondent and ready to give up. I asked her what she ate everyday – breakfast, lunch and dinner. She started by saying cheerfully, 'Aloo parathas and lassi.' I nearly fainted. As we progressed I realized what the real problem was – ignorance. Here was a woman who didn't have a clue about calories or diet types or her own body! How could

she possibly lose weight if she hadn't the foggiest idea of which foods suited her and what kind of exercise routine would get the results? This needs common sense – not high-flying personal trainers or nutritionists. Surely she should have known how fattening ghee-soaked aloo parathas are? You don't need to be a rocket scientist to figure out the richness of mithai or to avoid deep-fried foods (like pakoras), junk food (stay away from those pizzas!), French fries, puris, jalebis, rasgullas – I could go on and on. Do you get what I'm driving at? In these days of manic fitness programmes on virtually every TV channel, where small talk revolves around little else but weight loss or gain, this sort of information is accessible and known to anybody who cares to find out a little about 'good' and 'bad' foods. My neighbour does exercise, but she also has no self-control!

I can't emphasize this point enough – when it comes to stuffing your face, self-censorship is the only way to discipline the appetite. For those whose willpower is weak, I suggest a reward and punishment approach. Start by creating a simple chart. Define your objectives. Make a weekly calorie planner (ballpark figures will do). If you stick to your targets at the end of seven days, reward yourself. This reward could be a small indulgence (a piece of dark chocolate) or a bigger one (that bag you've been lusting after). Conversely, if you fail you must pay a fine – give up the movie, forget the glass of wine and postpone buying those jeans – you won't fit into them anyway! Unless you 'fine' yourself for defaulting, the plan will fall apart. Keep yourself motivated and upbeat. If you lapse into depression, cheat on the calories, are consumed by guilt or allow stress to get the better of you, just make peace with your God-given silhouette and forget about changing a thing. Be defiant and tell the world, 'Love me, love my bulges!' I know several women who have settled for that and are so much happier than they were fighting a losing battle against kilos that refused to miraculously disappear. A happy woman (give or take a few inches) is a better person to live with than a perennially tense, exercise-obsessed demon who growls, rarely smiles and snaps each time someone mentions 'F' from 'food'.

From the 'F-word' to the dreaded 'B-word'. 'B' for 'botox'. 'L' for 'liposuction'. 'S' for 'surgery'. Let me state it straight up – I am against intrusive interventions of any kind. Going under the knife is simply not an option in my book. But, if that is what you want for yourself and if a competent surgeon can give you what nature didn't, that's up to you. I have seen women who emerge looking twenty years younger after getting 'fixed up', and others who look like a truck hit them head on. Botoxed smiles, silicon breasts and liposuctioned butts have given a new life to countless women worldwide. In India too, the number of women surgically altering/enhancing their bodies is going up. My better sense tells me these procedures have to be undertaken after careful consideration and enough research, if at all. However, if any woman believes her self-esteem will shoot up if she experiments with her body, so be it. Being compulsively pro-nature, I would personally attack such issues via less drastic means. Different strokes for different folks. I have met ladies who have told me their miserable lives turned around for the better after they chopped, cut, sliced and carved up some unattractive body parts. They started enjoying their clothes much more and their mirrors told them what they needed to hear most, 'You're hot!'

My youngest daughter Anandita, who is twenty-one, is a great inspiration to all of us. My older children blame me squarely for having mollycoddled her as a child. Since she was (and remains) the baby of the family, I guess I did what most mothers do – I overfed her. I'd watch those limbs turn plump and firm, and congratulate myself on a job well done. I fed her round the clock without thinking even once about the long-term consequences. By the time she turned five, she resembled a mini pumpkin. The fat was there to stay. I watched in alarm as she moved into her pre-teens, unable to participate actively in physical activities that demanded stamina and agility. I felt terrible and I felt guilty – I knew I had brought this on her. I also knew that if I worked on her vanity in a sensible and sensitive way, she'd become aware of her frame and want to do something about it. The trouble was, I had introduced her to 'bad' food at an early age. Anandita was never ever obese, but she wasn't fit either. Compared to her slim and toned siblings she stood out at family gatherings, and was subject to some nasty comments like, 'Oh my God! Look at your sisters and look at you!' I would cringe each time this happened since I knew I was the one to blame.

By the time she was a teenager, she herself was starting to resent her body but was still unwilling to do anything about it. Food became an obsession with her and because she was aware of the entire family's concern, she began to eat on the sly. Meal times were tense and traumatic as she'd barely touch anything on the table. Of course, we knew her secret – she would later go to the club and binge. We had countless tearful confrontations on the issue – I was astonished and angry at myself for having let this happen. All that cheese, ghee, pasta, potatoes – oh God – I had stuffed her with rubbish! Me! Someone who prided herself on knowing enough about nutrition never to make such mistakes.

Suddenly, one fine day when she was a few months away from her seventeenth birthday, Anandita arrived at a major decision. She decided she was going to lose weight. She set a target for herself and announced it to all of us. We were delighted, but rather sceptical. Her weight loss goal seemed unrealistic and impossible to achieve – eighteen kilos in four months? I sat her down and we discussed the various downsides of rapid weight loss. I told her never to starve herself, throw up or take diet pills (they kill!). She promised she'd do it sensibly and responsibly, but do it she would. There was a steely determination in her eyes. She joined a gym and planned a punishing

regimen, but most importantly she acknowledged for the very first time that she was indeed overweight. This was a major breakthrough since till that point she'd always gaze at herself in a full-length mirror and see a slim person. She really and truly had not thought she needed to lose a single kilo or inch. She felt everybody was just being 'mean' to her. Well. That was the beginning, and guess what? Today, four years later, Anandita looks just fabulous. She is well proportioned, confident, fit and *aware*. She knows the foods that suit her and which to avoid. She adheres to a routine that is appealing, not punishing which is really the key to maintaining yourself. I have learned so much, thanks to Anandita. I can never emulate her discipline when it comes to working out but I can definitely appreciate her positive attitude. She now thinks differently about health and fitness. If she skips a few sessions at the gym she does not go into a neurotic tail spin. Her obsession with food surfaces from time to time but she doesn't binge eat – if only the rest of us had such will power!

I never did have a perfect body, not even in my modelling years, but somehow it did not bother me. I made my peace with all the imperfections and decided to focus on my better attributes. Therein lies the trick; women who acknowledge their physical shortcomings can then work on highlighting other better aspects of their bodies. We are born with a certain frame. My bone structure makes me wide hipped and that's that. There is nothing I can do to alter my body type. But what I can do is try and ensure I don't pile on the kilos on my hips. It is very tough to keep those particular kilos off, since my vocation demands I remain seated for long hours at a desk. There is minimal physical activity in my life and the extra inches that settle below the waist after a certain age are hard to dislodge. To make it easier for myself, I concentrate on basic asanas that stretch the muscles around the midriff, thighs and hips. I wear clothes that distract attention from my hips and enhanced my torso. This means I could never wear skinny jeans, waist-skimming t-shirts, tight skirts or flared ghagras but so be it! All my clothing-related decisions are taken keeping this handicap in mind. Sarees are a staple in my wardrobe, since I find them the most flattering garment for Indian figures (most of us are hip-heavy). I feel graceful clad in a saree but I do not ever make this a camouflage or use it as a 'cover-all-my-flaws' excuse to let go – I still want to keep my options open. I am very experimental with my clothes and do not want to deprive myself of the pleasure of switching styles. This is incentive enough to keep those hips in check!

The important aspect of understanding your body type and silhouette is to be brutally frank with yourself. You have to come to terms with what cannot be fixed, except via drastic surgical intervention though, as I said earlier, I absolutely do not believe in cosmetic surgery that is done for further beautification, and would never ever recommend it to anyone I call a friend! Once you make your peace with your body you stop fretting and start living. Here are some suggestions worth following:

1. Know what suits your frame and experiment with garments that flatter you within those parameters.

2. Focus attention on areas that need to be moulded like flabby arms or lax abdominal muscles through exercise. Remember, spot reduction is far harder than losing weight overall. The results are slower too.

3. Pay close attention to your diet – is it balanced? Enough fibre? Enough NUTRITION? Believe it or not, but I have met women from the upper echelons of society who are victims of malnutrition without realizing it. Because of crazy fad diets and incorrect advice from self-styled fitness gurus, women frequently fall into the quick-fix trap – weight-loss programmes that promise instant results through drastic methods like plastic body wraps. Sure, you lose weight visibly and dramatically, but at what cost? The body is an intricate machine and every organ is interdependent on countless other mechanisms that keep us functioning smoothly. By reducing the water content radically, the weighing scales will register a loss of a couple of kilos all right, but the other loss, of essential minerals and salts in that water, can cause enormous harm to the system. 'Just bananas' types of diets are equally bad for the

body. Malnutrition sets in because of the imbalance created by such an approach. If the body is starved of any essentials, it reacts in ways that are hard to predict. A close friend suffering from chronic pain in her joints discovered after a series of agonising tests that there was a serious vitamin deficiency attacking her bones, since her standard diet was so lopsided and irregular.

4. Listen to granny. Nearly all that I know about my body and mind is knowledge received from my elders. The basic Indian diet has evolved over centuries and, like anything that endures over time, is based on sound fundamentals. It is practical, balanced and in tune with our climate. I can tell you about my own Maharashtrian cuisine, which is in my book one of the healthiest cuisines in the world along with the south Indian one. The medium of cooking here is water, not oil. Oil is sparingly used for just the tadka. Vegetables are lightly steamed and delicately spiced with no heavy masalas. Chappatis and *bhakris* are made from rough hand-ground atta that is either whole-wheat, bajra or jowhar. Dahi accompanies both main meals, and raw salad (tomatoes, cucumbers and white onions) is a must. Rice is consumed in smaller portions, while the dal is often made from pulses soaked overnight that have sprouted. Most sweets have a base of hung yoghurt. Meat is restricted to a weekend treat, while fish is rarely deep-

fried. Some would call this a bit frugal but I'd say it is perfectly balanced. One rarely meets overweight Maharashtrians! All the good stuff grannies pass on is basically distilled experience over generations. Home remedies are what I swear by. Indian herbs are being discovered by the rest of the world in the twenty-first century. We have always known their virtues but have been short-sighted enough to ignore their potential and use. I always rely on the multiple benefits (medicinal and cosmetic) of the tulsi plant. I begin my day by drinking a glass of warm water with five or six tulsi leaves floating in it, along with a teaspoon of raw honey. Not only is this a great detoxifier and pick-me-up, but the tulsi and honey combination acts as a filter against high pollution levels and protects my throat against infections. Honey also heals wounds, burns in particular, while tulsi is truly a miracle herb that our sages used to cure a multitude of conditions. Ditto for haldi – turmeric root is one of the best disinfectants. My fridge is a reliable friend. When in doubt, I raid the fridge! These days it is stuffed with what are called 'superfoods' – broccoli, red and yellow peppers, pumpkin, leafy vegetables, sprouts and lots of dahi. Dahi and lassi keep the brain alert and the calories off. I have both round the year. Since I rarely visit a beauty salon (when was the last time I had a professional facial? Five years ago?), I follow my own regimen. The best face packs in the world are created from kitchen ingredients – mashed fruits, fresh cream, dahi, cucumber and lemon juice. All you need is a little imagination combined with some knowledge of your particular skin type.

Grannies did not have their pampering done in fancy salons and spas – their spas were in their own homes. From hot-oil hair massages to herbal baths and loofah scrubs, granny did it all on her own – with spectacular results to show for it too. I prefer sticking to traditional remedies myself. I have discovered a great exfoliating medium – channa dal mixed with *malai*. I massaged all my children with the mixture, and today they all have healthy, glowing skin. I unfortunately no longer use this mixture since my skin is far more sensitive today than it was when I was in my thirties.

Skin changes with age and hormonal shifts. The products that worked for you in your twenties may not do the job in your forties. Listen to your skin, it speaks to you. Mine always tell me when it is thirsty or hungry. Since dry skin has always been a problem, I rehydrate mine frequently. Till recently I used to exfoliate it daily with rice powder mixed in malai but realized how harsh and abrasive the process was when my skin began to protest. I asked a dermatologist what the problem was – why was my skin so itchy, dry and flaky these days? She told me that with age skin becomes thinner and more fragile. Any friction leads to damage which shows up in the form of dark patches or even an angry rash. She

also warned me against scrubbing my face with a hand towel after I washed it: 'Always pat it dry. Don't ever wipe your face briskly with hard movements or you'll hurt the capillaries just under the surface.' It was an important tip since I was so used to a brisk rub, under the false assumption that I was taking care of blackheads and giving my face an invigorating workout in the bargain. Far from it! My poor skin had been subjected to cruelty for years. I promptly discontinued the old routine and am much gentler these days. Sunblock theories abound. I am a new convert, so I can be forgiven for swearing by it. The sun has a powerful effect on skin, as we all know. But what I wasn't aware of was just how damaging the harsh rays of the sun can be on unprotected skin. Most times, mature skin develops ugly sun spots because of the absence of sunblock. Ever since I started to use it a few months ago, I have noticed a marked difference in my skin tone. Not only is it more even, but those unsightly patches are that much lighter and therefore less noticeable.

SKINCARE IN THE SIXTIES

Ladies, this is difficult to accept or put into practise but once you do, life becomes that much easier – accept the lines on your skin. There is nothing to be ashamed of once you tell yourself that each line has its own story to narrate. Some of these stories may be pleasant, some not so, and that's life. It's when you start fighting these lines that something strange happens – they seem to multiply! If you leave them alone they may not disappear, but at least they won't proliferate. Stress is the culprit and stress it is that creates those lines. In the old days they were called 'wrinkles'. A wrinkled woman was made to feel unattractive by society at large with *buddhiya* (old woman) being a nasty put-down. Today, millions are spent on cosmetic research that focuses on anti-ageing products, but let me tell you bluntly and candidly: nothing works. The skin degenerates just like the rest of the body. So far, nobody has been able to discover anything that regenerates old skin. One can only delay the process a little via a life-long regimen of skincare, but it has to start early.

I became aware of the need to cleanse my skin scrupulously in my twenties. Today, there are a number of really expensive products that are supposed to do the job, soap and water won't do. Soaps can be very harsh on tender skin, as is witch hazel. So what is the ideal cleanser for mature skin? I would say the mildest face gels or baby products. I prefer the latter. I'm also partial to unscented glycerine soaps. These soaps suit most skin types and work effectively to rid the body of any grime. Since most women today use some eye make-up (liner, shadow, mascara), it is important to remove all traces of it before going to bed. Baby oil works best to do this and it is safe to use as well. Cold make-up removal pads also do wonders to brighten tired eyes. I soak these cotton pads in ice-water and place them over my eyelids as an instant pick-me-up when I've removed every trace of make-up. I also love spraying pure rose water over my

face first thing in the morning – it is such a fragrant way to greet the day!

Creams come in various categories, and since I know my skin suffers from dryness, I opt for lanolin-rich products that get rapidly absorbed. Through a process of trial and error, one can always find a skin cream that soothes and replenishes tired skin. It is important to remember that no cream can actually eliminate lines once formed. As for regular facials, I am somewhat sceptical as to whether they really help. The skin certainly feels pampered after a lavish caviar facial, and there can be a momentary glow that gives the illusion of the texture being altered. In reality, this is nothing but a short-term high: women who are addicted to facials confirm they emerge from a salon feeling heavenly but the very next morning their faces are back to the original condition. I feel there's no harm in indulging in a facial from time to time if it relaxes you. A tense face adds ten years to a woman while a worried frown creasing the brows can age your face in an instant. So, relax and smile. A genuine smile that reaches the eyes can light up a room. Research has established that people who smile more than they scowl are likely to succeed in whichever situation – domestic, professional or personal.

Smiling for success may seem a simplistic solution but try it. Remember, a good smile involves clean teeth and healthy gums! In the old days people (women in particular) only visited a dentist if they needed a root canal or if they were born with buck teeth.

Today, it is all about having cosmetically perfect teeth! I am not for the plastic porcelain smile at all. I happen to like my slightly crooked teeth as they give me individuality. For women who want to enhance their appearance, it is possible to get uneven teeth capped and shiny. A smile must reach the eyes and light up the entire face – that's what brings a sparkle to the personality. But a smile that makes another person smile back has to be a genuine one – it must come from the heart. I feel fortunate that I still have much to smile about on a daily basis. It takes very little to make me smile. Sometimes, when I catch sight of myself on a reflective surface and observe the ferocious frown of concentration, I immediately (and consciously) relax my forehead muscles and focus on something that makes me smile. Women who obsess over 'smile lines' or 'crow's feet' should realize how much softer their face looks when they are happy, never mind those creases in the corners of their eyes.

More important than just the cosmetic appeal of a great smile is basic hygiene. I grew up in a home where we could not as much as greet our parents without first brushing our teeth. The brushing routine itself was very prolonged and thorough. These were pre-flossing days, but we were encouraged to examine our teeth in a mirror and get rid of any food particles stuck in them. These early habits ensured that I have strong teeth and healthy gums to this day! My grandmother and mother both passed away with their original thirty-two teeth in good condition. My mother

(lovely smile) would declare proudly, 'See, no dentures!' Her nightly rituals were something all of us emulated scrupulously. Once we'd brushed our teeth post-dinner, nothing in the world could tempt us to nibble, not even the yummiest, gooiest chocolate fondant. This rule remains in force today as well. I hope my children will not be lazy and cheat – I keep flashing my 'clean teeth' to demonstrate the results of life-long dental care. In case you are guilty of neglecting your teeth, I recommend a quick trip to the dentist. There's nothing like getting an expert opinion. If a gum-and-teeth-cleansing routine is recommended, don't put it off. Gum infections affect various other areas of your body, and the bacteria hidden inside those cavities can cause a myriad infections that you may not connect to spongy gums. It all begins with oral hygiene – floss away diligently, preferably after every meal. Remember tea and coffee leave awful stains on the teeth. Red wine is a culprit too. Rinse your mouth after eating anything, even fruit. It takes less than a minute but will save you hours of painful dental work later.

But honestly speaking, the best kept beauty secret in the world does not come out of a jar. It is love. Give it generously, and keep glowing.

CHAPTER 5

The Big, Fat, Major Change

The best part of the art of living
is to know how to grow old gracefully.

— *Eric Hoffer*

*M*uch has been written about menopause but very little is actually known, especially by women who believe they are too young to be menopausing but are, in fact, right in the middle of what is euphemistically described as 'The Change'.

For starters, drop the euphemism and address this deeply sensitive phase of your life with the seriousness it deserves. Examine your own attitude towards menopause – does the word embarrass you? Are you afraid of what menopause entails? Do you feel ashamed that you'll become less of a woman post-menopause? Once you identify your attitude to the subject and confront what is inevitable, you will be able to tackle it much better. The fact of the matter is that women are menopausing at a younger and younger age. Experts on the subject insist that this has to do with drastic environmental changes as well as lifestyle upheavals in the twenty-first century. Stress is often cited as a factor along with the fact that more and more women are delaying marriage, postponing babies or simply nixing both options. Our hormones are going crazy, unable to cope with all these issues. Even those women who have lived conventionally are finding it difficult to reconcile the onset of menopause in their lives, regardless of the age it first manifests itself.

HOW DO YOU KNOW YOU ARE ABOUT TO MENOPAUSE?

The first signs are missed periods. Of course, this sign has to be seen in the context of several other symptoms such as mood swings, hair loss, erratic appetite, dark patches on the skin, etc. Remember to catch these as soon as they appear but don't be in a hurry to categorize them as pre-menopausal symptoms. Make sure you visit your gynaecologist to rule out any other medical condition, fibroids in particular. Once you know that it is not any of the above and your doctor gives you the 'all clear', tell yourself that you are ready to confront the next important turning point of your life – menopause. Don't psyche yourself out and don't let it scare you. Think of it as the most natural evolutionary process that has to be taken in your stride, just as you took in all those other equally dramatic changes like menstruation and childbirth. Think of menopause as the end of one cycle and the beginning of another. If your thoughts remain positive, you will be able to deal with it that much better.

My own feelings started off being slightly mixed. I was fifty plus when my otherwise clock-work regular periods started to play hooky from time to time. Since I shared a superb rapport with my gynaecologist, she was my first stop. After a thorough examination, she told me to relax – it was nothing more than the first sign of menopause. We discussed the subject at length and agreed that while I would monitor my periods henceforth, I would not make any attempt to regulate them through pills or other interventions. I told her frankly that I was against Hormone Replacement Therapy (HRT), which was very popular with my generation. My reservations had to do with the fact that mine was amongst the first batch of women to be guinea pigs for these drugs which were meant to 'ease the trauma' of menopause and make our lives qualitatively better than our mothers' or grandmothers'. Nothing was known at that stage about the harmful side-effects of the treatment and I was not prepared to take any chances. Just because countless ladies across the world were busy singing praises of this miracle therapy, I wasn't about to fall for the ruse. I reasoned that if generations of women before me had gone through menopause without any fuss, why interfere with nature? For centuries, women had dealt with this drastic period (let nobody tell you it isn't drastic) and accepted it as a part of life. I was also going to face it, with all its downsides, and see how I'd hold up.

Let me tell you truthfully, it wasn't easy. There were times I felt suicidal and as if my life was spinning out of control. I'd feel depressed and defeated, touchy and teary for nothing. I couldn't explain it to myself, even though I realized on a conscious level that what I was actually battling against was what I had mentally accepted – menopause. But the emotional response was different; it was out of my control. I felt powerless, helpless and stupid. I would experience mood swings that my rational self would condemn but my heart would condone. It was a crazy period. There were weeks when I'd feel completely fine, and then without the slightest warning I'd be hit by a gathering storm and boom – I'd be ready to climb walls. Even worse, other people would be driven into climbing walls too. Menopause is hard on families. I had sat mine down and explained the process to them, emphasizing that there could be hours/days/months during which I'd turn into a monster. Sure enough, I did! I say this shamefacedly, for I was aware of the pitfalls all along but could do nothing about my irritability. I considered yoga, meditation, deep breathing, joining a gym – anything but medication. I soon realized that the solution lay within. I was determined to lick the blues and stay sane. There were countless lapses but it wasn't all that bad. Once I could see a fog of depression approaching I would mentally prepare for it and distract myself by watching a movie, calling up a friend or stepping out with the children. It was when

The Big, Fat, Major Change

I surrendered to the morose feelings that I'd lapse into a state of inertia and (worse) self-pity. Menopause is difficult to deal with, let's face it, but deal with it we must. For a few fortunate women it's over before they realize it. For others, it often involves drastic symptoms – hot flushes, cramps, night sweats, pigmentation and weight gain. A sensible, balanced diet (preferably a natural, vegetarian one rich in iron) helps the body to regain its balance a little faster. Since I did not experience hot flushes, I escaped the embarrassment other women told me about. But I did wake up on several nights drenched to the skin in perspiration, my hair damp and my nightclothes wet. It was such an unpleasant, clammy feeling that I'd clamber out of bed and swiftly change into something drier. At such times, the only thing that really helped was fresh air and my favourite cologne. My friends talked about ice packs and eye masks but I didn't bother with either.

My menopause stretched over two years. I know women who battled with it for as long as ten! Just when I thought it was finally over and was ready to throw a party, I spotted! My heart sank. I groaned as I set up an appointment with my doctor, who told me it was probably a one-off thing, but to monitor my monthly cycle scrupulously nevertheless. I was afraid of fibroids but she assured me I didn't have to worry about them. I spotted twice or thrice after that, and then I was free! Free from that tension-filled period when I'd find myself laughing or crying, or both, in a helpless way. For someone who is reasonably in control of her emotional conduct, this was most disconcerting. I used to think I was going mad. Why was I giggling? Or weeping?

This is where family support really counts. In my case, they rallied around splendidly. I felt protected and cocooned during this trying and often traumatic period, because those with whom I share my life were aware and non-judgemental about my behaviour. Talking about what I was going through made it possible to cope with the confusion. It also made it easier for my family to accept the erratic behaviour. Now when I look back, I realize how much I must have tried everybody's patience. I feel grateful that they put up with me so patiently, so lovingly.

It also made me reflect on the very first time I menstruated and how ill-prepared I was for that development. Of course, I knew all about 'periods' or 'chums' as it was called. I'd watched my elder sisters deal with it but had never really discussed it with my mother. It used to be such a taboo subject in those days. I only know that when it did happen I confided almost shamefacedly in my sister, who informed my mother, who in turn slapped her forehead in disgust and made me feel like a calamity had befallen me and the family. Since I was a sportswoman, I handled my periods without the slightest fuss. Being super active took my mind off the inconvenience, and I did not let the periods inhibit me from participating in any physically demanding activity or competing in the toughest athletic events.

When I experienced cramps, I refused to pop pills, preferring the relief provided by an old-fashioned hot-water bottle. This is what I advise my daughters as well, but do they listen? No. They pop pills, all sorts of painkillers that I know will play havoc with their systems. They also manipulate their periods by misusing pills to delay them. This is irresponsible and dangerous, but like they say, 'Everybody does it, and it's fine.' No, it is NOT fine! You are interfering with nature's cycle and whenever you do that, there are heavy consequences to deal with. Of course having periods is messy and a nuisance, but with the sort of personal hygiene products available in the market young girls really have no excuse to be careless on any front. Here again there is a plethora of options, with wafer-thin but highly absorbent sanitary towels easily available. I am against the use of tampons (at any age), but that's a matter of personal preference. Changing both sanitary towels and tampons at regular intervals is key – there is nothing as offensive as odour emanating from soiled sanitary towels. Keeping your private parts washed, dry and scrupulously clean at all times (particularly so during periods) is another must. Teenagers need instruction here, and it must be given as not adhering to these basics of cleanliness can lead to various infections.

The emotional roller coaster ride associated with periods is another story. Some women handle those four or five days with complete grace, while others go ballistic. Since PMS (Premenstrual Syndrome) is now a well-recognized condition, one must address it and ensure that women are made aware of what it entails, apart from the mood swings. I know friends who claim they used to feel suicidal before, during and after their periods. Two of my own daughters can barely crawl out of bed during those difficult days and spend most of their waking hours in bed doubled up with cramps, clutching a hot-water bottle and, worst of all, popping painkillers. Another one takes her periods in her stride, goes to the gym, plays games and is comfortable throughout. Most women outgrow cramps by the time they are in their mid-twenties. Those raging hormones get sufficiently tamed and the 'curse' (as it used to be called) doles out less harsh a monthly punishment.

The time between adolescence and menopause can stretch to thirty years and is the time in a woman's life when she is obliged to fulfil most of her roles and responsibilities. Chances are she marries, has children, enjoys a career and leads a busy, full and productive life. It is also the time she sometimes forgets to address her own specific physical and emotional needs. Even when it comes to health issues, women tend to give low priority to themselves, especially if the family budget is restricted. This can take a tremendous toll on them. My concern here is for a woman's holistic sense of wellness. If she ignores symptoms and allows herself to fall sick, she ends up doing a disservice not just to herself but to her entire family. It is important for mothers to make young daughters aware of this possibility so that they can safeguard themselves against such an eventuality.

Fortunately for us, awareness levels are pretty high these days with even the average housewife knowing enough about diets and good health. If she uses this practical knowledge to plan balanced meals for herself and her family, it can lead to a qualitative change in the entire family's lifestyle.

My own mother ensured we ate nutritional meals, and that we ate them on time. I have to emphasize the time factor here since these days we all like to imagine our lives to be so very hectic that we are forced to skip meals in order to save time. This is complete nonsense. Planning the day in a practical manner ensures that no meal has to be skipped. My mother used to start us off on the right note by producing a filling breakfast that saw us through till lunch time. For my father, breakfast used to be the most important meal of the day, and he continued to eat a hearty breakfast right till his last days (he passed away at the age of ninety-eight). He was a great believer in the goodness of eggs, which he had either boiled or fried every morning. There are several contradictory theories about the cholesterol in eggs, but I continue to be a fan. These days, however, I avoid eating eggs on a daily basis and restrict my intake to one, maximum two, a week. Most 'eggetarians' get their proteins from eggs, which are affordable even for lower-income families. Indian breakfast foods like the Maharashtrian *poha* make better nutritional sense than zero-value cornflakes. If you are a fan of cornflakes, I recommend you try oatmeal porridge in its place. I swear by porridge, and I'm sure it has saved many a woman's married life by seeing her through her low periods. Porridge is comfort food at its best; it is easy to prepare, easy to digest and an instant energy booster. One can even add oats to soup to form a nourishing and complete meal, especially during any kind of sickness where there is a loss of appetite and the sight of regular food makes the stomach turn. Single women coping with demanding jobs often rely on porridge at dinner time, or combine it with dal. Given its fibre content it really is the ideal food at any age and stage. In India, we have our own version of porridge. It's called *daliya* and works on the same principle – high fibre.

Milk products, again, have their pro- and anti-lobbies. I'm all for milk for babies and senior citizens. If milk suits your system, don't deny yourself. Milk has several virtues. People across India get their nutrition from milk – even the poorest family will try and ensure that their elders and children get their daily quota of milk. In north India, it is customary in winter for families to begin their day with a gigantic tumbler of hot milk, to which a generous garnish of dry fruits has been added. Breakfasts during the cold season are rich and lavish with aloo parathas smothered in pure ghee, and sweetmeats like jalebis eaten with fresh cream. Down south, where winters are far milder, milk products are consumed throughout the year – especially curd and its variants. Processed cheese is an urban habit but unprocessed cheese (paneer) is consumed across the country, especially in Kolkata, which creates most of its mouth-watering sweets like rasgullas and sandesh out of *chhena* (paneer or whey or hung curd). Milk allergies are pretty widespread too. My advice to young mothers who panic when their babies refuse milk, or break out into rashes after drinking it, is to find a substitute like soya milk.

FOOD AND MOOD SWINGS

Food and mood swings are interlinked, especially when a girl is menstruating and a woman is menopausing. In India, we have various theories revolving around what are called 'heating' foods. These are groups of food that cause the body to respond adversely to them which is why traditionalists recommend 'cooling' foods to women who are pregnant or menopausing. I am unsure whether or not there is a scientific basis for these theories, but common sense tells me that that if they have endured over centuries there has to be some foundation to them. Pregnant ladies are invariably advised to avoid eating papayas. Old wives' tales insist that eating papayas when pregnant leads to a miscarriage. Why? Who knows? For the same reason, a woman undergoing menopause should stay away from oily, over-spiced and deep-fried food (she should stay away from it regardless of her bio-cycles!).

I recall I couldn't digest any of these foods during this extended phase, and my body provided the right signals – I lived on salads, nuts (I swear by walnuts and almonds), fruits, steamed vegetables and fish, lightly cooked chicken and other bland dishes that my system felt comfortable with. In any case, one tends to bloat (or feel bloated) and as any woman will tell you – feeling bloated is sometimes worse than being bloated. It's strange how we women link our well-being to entirely irrational feelings. We can always blame that on our crazy hormones.

SEX AND MENOPAUSE

Menopause is a particularly delicate phase in a woman's life and it is very important for her partner to be sensitive to it. This is asking for too much perhaps, given that the average period from the onset of menopause till it's over can last for five years or more. To begin with, a woman has to deal with her own confusions and upheavals. She may feel unattractive and ugly, even though to the rest of the world she looks the same. If her self-worth takes a severe beating and she feels wretched about her body, she will naturally lose her enthusiasm for sex. Combine that with physical fatigue, mood swings and other changes and her love life goes straight for a toss. This can be the lowest, most discouraging period of her life, and particularly so if her partner makes her feel rejected and unattractive. I have met so many women who have felt suicidal during this long and arduous period. They've mentioned being put off by any attempts at sexual intercourse, while craving affection, cuddling and stroking that is all strictly non-sexual. They longed for physical intimacy but abhorred sexual intimacy, making it very difficult for their partners who could not decode the mixed signals. Was the wife snuggling up in bed actually initiating sex or was she looking for reassurance? Any wrong move at this point from the man would lead to arguments and fights, with both partners accusing one another of gross insensitivity.

Since the hormone levels do play havoc with you, it is better to switch your mind from sexual matters to something else that is distracting and involves physical activity. Long walks, swimming, golf and yoga definitely act as de-stressers, besides taking care of those extra calories. Lethargy can set in, but if it becomes habitual then those extra kilos will be that much harder to knock off. This is the touch-and-go time when women put on excess weight and feel wretched about it. Being aware is step number one. Why feel wretched at all? On the contrary, my advice is to selfishly focus on yourself and try your best to look good. You should make that extra effort to not let yourself go. Dress well, concentrate on basic grooming, and look after your skin (watch out for those dark, butterfly patches under the eyes), hair (regular oil massages), nails and eyes (bags can be treated with ice packs, used tea bags, slices of cucumber or sleep). Tell yourself it isn't the end of the road; it really isn't and you must believe it. Remain positive, knowing that once you finish menopausing, you are free. This is exactly what I did, and though it wasn't easy it worked for me, as it will for you.

Take time off to review your life and your priorities. This is the best time to do it – a new journey is beginning, and you must prepare for it. Your body, face and mind are never going to be the same again. Accept that for starters. On the upside, you will be permanently worry-free regarding unwanted pregnancies, contraception issues and waiting for supposedly safe days to enjoy sex. By now, you ought to be entirely comfortable and clued-up about your own sexual needs and preferences. If you are with the same partner, it will make it that much simpler to frankly discuss your attitude to sex during menopause. Some women actually start enjoying sex much more since they are no longer tense about making 'mistakes' or consulting the calendar. Since they are more at ease, their partners also feel more confident, even experimental. Yes, it's true! Post-menopausal woman have admitted that their sex lives improved many times over since they felt more liberated and adventurous in bed! That's the upside – make the most of it. Holidays taken with your partner at this stage can be far more enjoyable as you both rediscover each other and find that you are more in tune, with the old anxieties behind you.

Remember to eat right and monitor your health. Women with a tendency towards high blood pressure or those who are diabetic have to be extra watchful. As do women whose mothers and grandmothers suffered from arthritis. Consult a family physician and structure a sensible diet that works around your lifestyle. Vitamin supplements have always been a part of my daily routine, but I'd say it's better to pop them on your doctor's advice. There are several contradictory theories about vitamin E capsules. I ignore them and have taken this vitamin ever since I turned forty. Ditto for vitamin C.

Once you teach yourself to regulate the physical aspects of menopause, turn to the spiritual and emotional ones. My view is, go with anything that works for you, anything at all that comforts and soothes you. I used to listen to Buddhist chants all day and I found them extraordinarily calming. Though I didn't alter my basic routine (I continued to write at the dining table for a good six to eight hours daily), the music in the background definitely helped me remain at peace. I tried meditation and soon gave it up because my mind was far too restless. I did, however, say my prayers regularly and chant mantras twice a day. I also followed religious rituals like offering flowers, lighting incense and ringing a small bell in front of Ganeshji, one after my bath in the morning, and one again at dusk.

In terms of re-prioritizing, I cut down on a great deal of what I call 'useless socializing'. Taking stock of the one commodity that is constantly in short supply, time, made me realize the futility of social interactions that in no way added value to my life. Once I stopped being sociable in the way I was during my thirties and forties, I automatically experienced the qualitative difference it made to my life. I would read, write, communicate with family members I may have neglected, introspect, spring clean (my mind, along with the wardrobe) and generally feel far more centred and true to myself. It was a change for the better and my body reflected it! With more sleep and better sleep, I felt and looked relaxed. Spending time by myself provided insights and answers to a myriad unsolved questions. I discovered the guru within me – I didn't have to search the world for a spiritual master or take instructions from a stranger. This was a fascinating self-revelation and it reinforced my belief in myself. I accepted that resources were now in my own hands – it was just a matter of recognizing and reallocating them now that my priorities had changed. I'd say it made me a far better person – more grounded, more realistic, more in control and better able to handle crises big and small.

The most rewarding experience came from reaching out to others who needed help at some level. I became far more conscious of the many things that made me more fortunate than millions of other people. Things I used to take for granted like money, position and health. I also discovered that it was okay to be vulnerable and not hide behind a fake screen of security and pride. As human beings, we need one another, we are dependent on each other and constantly in search of love. It's fine. It's even beautiful. I turned menopause around to make it work for me. Menopause has its own upside and it's up to each woman how she chooses to tap into it. Did I panic? Oh yes, I did. I remember on the eve of my fiftieth birthday (I was pre-menopausal and very touchy), I went off on an absolute impulse to the neighbourhood salon and chopped off my long hair. Just like that! It was a pretty radical decision, and my family was shocked. I don't really know why I did it – I guess I needed to shock myself! I must have been feeling desperately in need of a change, a makeover and this was it. No regrets. I quite enjoyed the new me, as also the mixed reactions the haircut generated. Most people hated it and advised me to grow back my hair. I saw the act as a throwback to my old rebellious self – the one who constantly bucked the system. It was good to reconnect with that familiar teenager who would frequently get into trouble with her father and school principal for doing something defiant or naughty. I had regressed, and it felt therapeutic, even wonderful! So many small changes were taking place simultaneously during this dramatic decade that from fifty to sixty was definitely a tumultuous ten years. I'm sure it is a common experience. Several women I know actually came into their own post fifty – by then, they had distinct personalities and knew their position within the family and the community at large. They appeared more confident and sure of themselves, having dealt with so many different turning points – their own and their family's. In today's times it means coping with divorce, death, widowhood, children, financial roller coasters, breakdowns, losses . . . but mainly, it involves dealing with age and ageing, the acceptance of the inevitable and your ability to deal with it.

Menopausal depression deserves an entire book to itself. I remember meeting a sensational-looking socialite, well into her late fifties at the time, and a picture of not just glowing health but vibrant sexiness. Since she is a few years older than I am, I was astonished to observe her perfect skin, hair, figure and good humour. How did she do it? There I was, mid-menopause, looking and feeling like a dish rag, and there was this diva dressed in a figure-hugging outfit, looking better than a million bucks. I knew her well enough to ask. She leaned across and whispered conspiratorially, 'Hormone replacement therapy, Prozac, lots of champagne and retail therapy. That's the combo. It works – try it!' I thanked her for her generous and candid advice. Unfortunately, it wasn't for me. Like I'd said earlier, I didn't want to become a guinea pig for first-generation drugs. I do have to admit, this remarkable woman still looks astonishingly attractive even though she is now on the wrong side of sixty-five. I like to believe that it's the unaffordable red wine she consumes. It could also be the champagne. Whatever it is, it works for her. It doesn't for me.

Not being a spa person, I get impatient being pampered. Yet there are ladies of leisure who can't live without their caviar facials and other equally decadent treatments. I met two of them in Delhi, and both admitted they were 'spa addicts'. They sweetly recommended I try their experience once a week saying, 'It will help you to gather your thoughts – your writing will get better! In that peaceful, soothing atmosphere you'll get a lot of new ideas.' That night I dreamt I'd joined the spa gang – and woke up with a start. I prefer inviting my regular *maalish-wali* to the house at an hour that is convenient to me. She is silent and strong. We don't exchange a word. She does her job efficiently and my strained shoulder (the laptop syndrome) feels great after her pummelling. Oh, did I just refer to the laptop? Well, it has changed my life. Till my sixtieth birthday, I remained totally techno-challenged and computer illiterate. I relied on my daughters to help me deal with my mail and more – they were recruited to key in my countless columns. Arundhati and Anandita (God bless them) obliged without protesting too much but they had their own exams to cope with and their own specific schedules. I used to feel like a tyrant breathing down their necks, constantly urging them to meet my deadlines. It was lopsided, inconvenient and totally unfair. I realized this but was helpless and confused. Till . . . the girls took matters into their own hands, pooled in their resources, asked their dad for extra money and got me my very own laptop. They literally threw me into the deep end of the pool and said, 'Mom you're on your own now. Enjoy.' I stared at the machine suspiciously. I was fascinated and scared at the same time. I also recognized it as a do-or-die moment. I had to take the plunge or I'd get hopelessly left behind.

My first few attempts were embarrassingly clumsy. I felt frustrated and upset watching the ease with which kids of eight and ten navigated the net and knew exactly what to do. My girls were helpful, but up to a point. They couldn't understand how their 'smart' mom was so dumb when it came to technology! Gradually, I started to get the hang of it. Now, I'm hooked. I urge every woman with access to computers to go ahead and conquer her phobia if she has one. Access to the big, wide world out there can transform your life in the most amazing way. It certainly transformed mine. I place my cellphone and laptop right up there with the most important Life Altering Facilitators. Today, when I talk to my daughter Arundhati in Paris via Skype or share emails with my son Aditya, I feel so connected to the space they occupy. I surf, chat, email and download with the rest and best of them. It has provided me a gateway to another universe.

The day I began writing my daily blog, I realized the awesome potential of connecting in an instant with like-minded people thousands of miles away. These virtual relationships with strangers have become a part of my daily routine, like the carrot juice I consume every morning. I love hearing from my regular 'blog *dosts*'. I love our easy, no-strings-attached banter and the honest feedback I receive to what I post. It is rejuvenating and refreshing to plug into young, charged-up minds who challenge every line, and often prove one wrong. Oh, the enviable courage of youth!

I have encountered enormous kindness and compassion from unknown people on my blog. I started this segment with a reference to my sore shoulder (the laptop syndrome) – I cannot tell you how many friends from across the world wrote in with helpful suggestions, remedies and tips ranging from yoga asanas to simple exercises. The concern was for more genuine than the lip service of people one meets frequently. I was so touched by the comments posted on the blog and so grateful to those who offered practical treatments. My shoulder is vastly better; what it needs is rest. I realize that, but I am a stubborn and foolish creature. Take away my communication tools (pen, pad, laptop) and I am morose. These are my special highs, and I feel thankful to my children for initiating me into the magical universe that we call the World Wide Web.

RELAX!

It is important to recognize relaxation techniques and options, especially during middle age. Music, movies, gardening, chess, tennis, walks, nature, healing, salsa, belly dancing, travelling, photography – whatever pumps up your happiness quotient and keeps those stress levels down. Like I said earlier, it is very important to identify what gives you joy. If it is spending time playing nanny to your grandkids, go ahead. Change those dirty diapers, put up with kiddy tantrums, deal with baby puke and baby poo. But, if you do not want to play granny/nanny be forthright and say so. As my own mother did. She was very clear about her priorities and told us, her children, that she was done with kid stuff. We were not to base any of our baby decisions on her being there as an unpaid ayah! We were shocked at first by her bluntness, but in retrospect, she was right in making her position perfectly clear.

There are women who love being grandmoms and do a great job

of it, with enormous patience and grace. My own attitude remains untested. I say give me your babies for a few short hours at a time (once they are potty-trained) and I'll be happy to take care of them, but I don't see myself putting my own life on hold and becoming a full-time *nani* or *dadi*. Babies become interesting only after they reach an interactive stage. I know I'm making them sound like a video game, but communication skills do alter the equation completely. Once a child can express himself or herself, the relationship becomes far more challenging. So it is with grandparenting. I do admit I am looking forward to it most actively and I hope to become a fun granny rather that a grumpy one. I want my grandchildren to seek out my company; I want to be their friend and counsellor. The mental receptivity is in place, I just hope I can cope with the physical demands of chasing an over-energetic toddler. My dream vacation at this point would be a relaxing cruise with my grandchildren (their parents' presence is optional!). I would love to read to them, watch movies and even party! Maybe I am romanticizing the reality and forgetting my own age!

THE POWER OF TOUCH

When I discuss relaxation techniques with women of my vintage, they all talk about New Age gurus and meditation techniques that go well beyond breathing deeply. I talk about touch therapy.

It's strange how rapidly we lose our tactile sense – well, not lose it physically, but psychologically. We rarely reach out and touch one another. Societies and cultures vary when it comes to touch. There are taboos to deal with that can't be easily ignored. Even in more open and progressive societies, the human touch takes a back seat. I have met lonely Europeans who've confessed they haven't been hugged or themselves hugged anybody in years! A lot of them keep pets to ward off loneliness . . . isn't that sad? When they pet their dogs or a cat comes and perches on their lap they feel loved, at least for those brief minutes. I have instructed all my kids to hug and kiss me as often as possible – but once a day is compulsory! If we sensitize ourselves to this basic human need we can do something about it, or else we may wither away craving that small gesture. A light, sympathetic touch over a tense, clenched first, for example, can make all the difference between an agitated state and the calm that comes with feeling cared for.

The same goes for eye contact – do you realize we've stopped making it? Our lives have become so cold and impersonal that we see without actually seeing. We hear but we don't listen. Big difference. It had started to happen to me – I would appear attentive but my mind would be elsewhere. At first I put it down to age and a wandering mind but then I realized it was more like a disconnect. I had turned away from my old self, the person who could actively engage with complete strangers, someone who was genuinely interested in others. This made me reflect on the changes in my own personality, and I realized I was withdrawing into my own world more and more, and switching off from others. Of course, it had to do with age and shrinking interests in things around me, but it also had a lot to do with indifference. Once I became conscious of this trait, I tried to change. To some extent I feel I have succeeded – I make eye contact while talking to people even if it is the elevator attendant. I also listen closely when someone speaks to me. That I forget the conversation promptly is another story but at least the old, rather rude blank stare has become history!

HEALTH AND WEALTH

As the cliché goes, health is wealth. Most of us wait till it is too late to enjoy whatever wealth we have accumulated during our productive, working years. We slog and slave away for decades and then when we finally think we are financially secure and ready to spend on ourselves, it is too late to travel or have fun – real fun! I remember the first ever cruise I went on was in the Caribbean, and I was travelling with my young daughter. We got on board with much excitement but as we looked around, we saw at least fifty senior citizens on wheelchairs being pushed by either nurses or relatives. My daughter's spirits tanked there and then, and to an extent, so did mine. Later, while talking to the cruise director, we were told that these old people were being given a 'treat' by their families – a treat that was funded by the elderly people's own savings! Some of them were too feeble to leave the ship for shore excursions and just stayed on board for the entire duration of the cruise, eating all their meals in their cabins. How very depressing. That's when I made up my mind that this fate had to be avoided at all costs! I would travel, spend my own money and enjoy myself. No point having the means but not the physical well-being to go with the money.

In India, we worry too much about the future. It is a national trait. We worry about intangibles and make ourselves sick. We are forever saving for a rainy day, even during the worst drought or through a heavy monsoon. We obsess over the next generation, but forget that we are alive and have the right to a good time as well.

So far, my fitness levels are okay. I am not overly preoccupied by them. I ran the mini-marathon (Dream Run) for a favourite charity just a year or two short of my sixtieth birthday. I hadn't trained for it and I certainly wasn't planning on breaking any records. I was just keen to participate and test my stamina. I made it! That was a big moment for me.

Since I am not big on annual health check-ups and avoid entering a doctor's clinic at all costs, I rely mainly on my own basic knowledge of personal wellness. I am pretty much in tune with my mind and body and can sense when something is wrong or likely to go wrong. I wouldn't recommend this approach to everyone since it can also backfire if you either miss or misread signals. I also believe that if you obsess over your health you turn into a health zombie – a freak who is constantly checking cholesterol levels, blood pressure and other parameters of health. To the extent possible, I say stay away from clinics and listen to your heart, literally. For instance, I know that when my stress levels are high I get acidity, leading to heartburn and poor sleep. It becomes a pretty vicious cycle during which I am acutely aware of a burning sensation in my throat and general discomfort. I alter my eating pattern instantly – that's just for starters. I avoid fried, spicy food but find it hard to give up white wine and champagne (my weakness!). I also start a short course of antacids to calm my stomach. What I sometimes neglect to do, despite being aware of the problem, is to calm my nerves. That's easier said than done. Since meditation is not an option for me, I try other de-stressing methods. I write feverishly, since for me writing is therapeutic and I love it. I listen to my favourite music, dance, or very occasionally give in to the oldest stress buster in a woman's book – retail therapy. The purchase does not have to be something pricey, even a fun bauble or inexpensive trinket will do. I get a thrill from small attractive objects that catch my fancy. It is about distracting the mind, howsoever briefly. Men find women's mood swings most confusing but we know exactly why we flip out sometimes, don't we? We really don't have to justify or explain each twitch, scowl or frown. That's how we are, okay?

CHAPTER 6

Sex with a Silver Lining!

Love is the answer,
but while you are waiting for the answer,
sex raises some pretty good questions.

– Woody Allen

*W*hen it comes to sex, that dangerous three-letter word, suddenly the floodgates are thrown open and emotional ambiguities tumble out.

Senior citizens in our culture are not supposed to entertain carnal desires or thoughts, forget about having sex! Sex is seen in the context of procreation, not pleasure. Once procreation ends, sexual desire has to be curtailed if not banished altogether. This is entirely false, as countless couples will readily confess. If the person is fit (reasonably so), has a positive attitude to sex and is not bogged down by society's rigid rules, the sixth decade can well turn out to be a sexually satisfying one, especially with a loving partner. By now both of you have settled into a familiar pattern and know each other's requirements (physical and emotional) intimately. There is no self-consciousness and nothing left to prove. You aren't there to rate his sexual prowess as a super stud, and he doesn't expect you to turn into a purring sex kitten either. Instead, you have moved into a comfort zone and feel relaxed enough to actually enjoy the experience sans tension. Many couples insist they feel more sexually attuned after fifty than they did earlier in their marriage.

Post-menopausal women admit to rediscovering their sexual potential once the hot flushes subside. Freed from the fear of an unwanted pregnancy, they are more willing to experiment and enjoy physical togetherness. Studies have revealed that long-term partners in monogamous relationships who continue to have sex in their sixties and seventies live longer, healthier lives. Perhaps it has to do with hormonal balances, but older women who have not turned their backs on sex definitely exude more vitality. It is a question of breaking through prejudice and freeing oneself of hang-ups ('Oh my God! What if the children find out? What will the grandkids think? Is it unnatural to want sex at our age?'). For one, couples at this stage have more leisure time, especially if they've opted for retirement. The frenzied, hectic years of their lives are generally behind them by now, and financial worries have been sorted out. This lowers tension levels and leads to a far mellower phase that can be successfully exploited by both partners in a more accepting way. Yes, the wife's breasts sag and aren't as firm as they used to be. Yes, the husband is balding and has a paunch. So what? If warmth and love can't make up for these shortcomings, fantasy definitely can! Shut your eyes and let your mind do the rest. Therapists these days advise the creative use of sex toys and erotic videos to pep up 'partner fatigue'. Well, whatever works!

Traditional societies discourage any expression of senior citizen sexuality. How can grandmas and grandpas have sex, they ask in shocked tones. Why not? Grandmas and grandpas don't cease to be alive, sensual beings just because there are grandkids in the picture! Western society deals with the same issue differently. There is a live-and-let-live attitude at work and nobody passes judgements on oldies enjoying sex. Perhaps this will change in India too, but at present people are reluctant to address the issue, leading to a great deal of embarrassment for all concerned. It is almost as if a woman is obliged to feel guilty if she entertains such ideas once her children are married. Men risk being called 'dirty old men' if they express interest in the subject. What I want to say is that sex in the sixties can be a joyful, fulfilling experience. The idea is to keep an open mind and not deny yourself the pleasure of a complete physical relationship just because society does not approve. However, I have also met a large number of women who insist they genuinely do not have the slightest desire to engage in any sexual activity after a certain point. Their feelings must also be respected.

Though the 'cougar' phenomenon is new to our society, its existence cannot be denied any longer. A cougar refers to a much older woman taking a fancy to a much younger man. Women in such relationships claim they enjoy the attention of their youthful partners and that their sex lives rock! Be that as it may, I notice that generally women who maintain a very active lifestyle – those who walk, exercise, play games, travel, swim, drive or work – seem to have a more positive self-image overall and do not deny themselves when it comes to enjoying sex. The same goes for men who value fitness and look after their physiques.

The one libido killer is (believe it or not) alcohol! Young couples may drink to enhance their sex life but as you age and tolerance levels for alcohol get lowered, what may start off as a promising evening of *l'amour* can crash with a resounding thud if the couple has knocked back a few. That is what is called a real anti-climax. So, watch the booze and go easy on the martinis. Alcohol is a depressant, contrary to popular perception. Besides, there is no greater turn-off for even the most loyal partner than beer-and-biryani breath in bed!

For those who think they are missing out on one of life's most beautiful experiences, my advice is to go for it! Don't feel shy. This is the time for stress-free explorations of your most intimate self. Go the whole hog if you have the resources. Take 'sex breaks' over weekends and make them romantic and memorable. Don't have

unrealistic expectations from one another. This is not about setting new records as athletes in a sex marathon. This is about closeness and enjoyment. Make it fun. Make it fulfilling! Get away from the routine of daily life. Think of sex as your best meditation and gradually you'll feel your body and mind experiencing delicious harmony, feeling at peace and feeling love . . .

What more do you want?

CHAPTER 7

Me First!

Living Up the Sixth Decade

Whenever the talk turns to age,

I say I am 49 plus VAT.

— *Lionel Blair*

*I*f you keep your goals realistic in your sixties anything and everything is achievable. These days I find myself working harder than ever before. It is turning out to be my most productive period to date. I feel on top of my time and on top of my life, all because I've decided to make the most of my sixth decade by reorganizing a few priorities.

Perhaps for the first time in years, I've started placing myself first in a few situations. As a young mother, I always put the children first. Then as a middle-aged wife, I put my husband first. It is only now that I've begun to place importance on my own personal priorities by saying, 'Me first!' Initially, I used to feel a bit self-conscious about this and wonder if I was being selfish. But today I feel I'm a far more efficient person than I was, and in the process my respect for other people's time has gone up as well. I look around me and see a lot of my contemporaries leading equally busy lives – clearly a big change has taken place in our society; a change for the better. I'm enjoying the sort of options my own mother never had. I am truly independent on every level and in a position to make informed choices. This is a privilege I value. At forty, I'd think twice before booking myself on a flight and taking off for a foreign destination. Today, I do that and more with the confidence that comes via experience. I urge other women to extend themselves and see how far that takes them. On my travels, I often run into like-minded ladies who have rediscovered forgotten passions and are pursuing them with energy and commitment. One particular lady, well into her seventies, is making up for lost academic ambitions by enrolling for summer courses at Harvard/Oxford and has imposed a strict rule on her amused but anxious family – strictly no visits during her six-week stay. She says firmly, 'I want these weeks solely for myself. My family should understand and respect that.' How wonderful and how satisfying! The limits we live with are generally those we impose on ourselves. My ardent wish is to stretch those old limits and see where that takes me.

My new goals remain realistic and down to earth – that's the key. I can no longer walk ten kilometres a day over cobblestones in Tuscany, so I forget about it. Why attempt something undesirable, potentially harmful and even impossible? I could learn karate for senior citizens, but do I want to? Wouldn't I prefer to invest the same time in exploring a brand new destination (Poland!) or in conducting creative writing classes for students at a university of my choice? My day is crammed with activities I enjoy and to me *that* is essential.

I am not a chronic worrier by nature, thank the good Lord, which means I don't spend hours brooding over something I have zero control over. Health and financial issues dominate at this stage, and I have taught myself to deal with both as calmly as possible. Planning for the future is one thing, but obsessing over all that could go wrong in the years ahead is quite another. It's easy to 'be sensible', but when a crisis crops up most of us forget about being sensible and give in to panic attacks.

Aah – panic attacks. Even the calmest people succumb to them as they grow older and their insecurities mount. For example: forgetfulness. I have a pretty good memory most of the time (as a writer it is essential) but these days I fail to remember minor details like where I left my glasses. Often they are found by someone else, perched on top of my head. I forget when I removed my jewellery after coming home from a function, or where I put it 'for safety' thereafter. I recently forgot where my daughter's passport had been stored, and that really threw me since I keep all the passports together in a locked drawer. Only hers was missing! After a frantic search, it was discovered at the travel agent's office where I'd sent it to process a visa. See what I mean? It is worrying, embarrassing and annoying. One of the several reminders that age is catching up with me and cannot be ignored. How do I resolve these issues? I have found that writing memos to myself is the only way for me to remember. I have turned into a Post-it devotee. Those tiny yellow slips are all over the place with instructions to myself 'not to forget'. The trouble is that I forget what I'm supposed to not forget. I make doubly sure to let one of my children know my 'to-do list'. Leaving things to memory alone is no longer the best option. My father used to say that it was a fascinating phenomenon that as the brain ages, old memories resurface vividly in sharp focus. At age ninety plus, he could effortlessly recall the details of his life in the district courts as a judge, but would forget a conversation we'd had just a few hours earlier! The trick is to be aware and conscious of this condition and work around it skilfully. I know, for instance, that I do not have a good head for numbers, including the numbers on the licence plate of my own car – I simply cannot get it to register in my head! So, what do I do? I train myself to look out for other visual signals that distinguish my car from someone else's. It could be a sticker, a dangler or even a tissue box. That's what I focus on, rather than committing the number to memory.

Most of us by this stage are on some medication or the other and are

used to swallowing a fistful of tablets – vitamin supplements, blood pressure pills and so on. Keeping a track of these and consuming them on time is a feat in itself. My solution: get a multi-compartment, clear plastic box so you can see the tablets after you separate them. If there is a daily cocktail you have to gulp down at breakfast, keep the lot together in a compartment with a sticker over it that reads 'BREAKFAST'. This is an easy system to follow, and requires only ten minutes of your time at the beginning of each month. I keep my daily doses within easy reach (right next to my laptop) along with a bottle of water so I have no excuse not to pop those pills. Since I hate dependency on medication, I keep the pills I need to a bare minimum. I have resisted taking any nerve calmers, tranquilizers or sleep-inducement remedies so far. On nights when my brain is in overdrive and sleep doesn't come easily, I don't fight it or stress over it. I surrender to my sleepless state. I close my eyes in a darkened room and think constructive thoughts. I use the bonus time to plan my morning or mentally tick-off neglected chores. I resist the temptation to switch on the light, get out of bed and wander towards my laptop, or even write. This is really tough since there are times when great ideas are flying out of my head at 3 AM. but I know that if I give in to that urge, I'll be writing till dawn and then my body will face the consequences later! My feet get restless, but I manage to talk them into not moving. I merely make myself as comfortable as possible, fluff up my pillows and recite a mantra or two. Sleep has to follow eventually . . . and generally does. A warm bath and jasmine tea are devices that work for some people but have never worked for me. Physical and mental fatigue makes my brain go into overdrive instead of tiring it out. Most people have the best sleep when they collapse into bed in an exhausted heap – lucky, lucky them!

So, ladies, admit it. The first time you heard your knees creak while bending to retrieve something it came as a bit of a shock, right? It's a sure sign that your skeletal system is under pressure and the years are creeping up on you but so what?

Face the situation squarely. Nobody escapes their fate, and you are not an exception. Creaking bones must not be ignored, especially if arthritis or osteoporosis runs in the family. Most women's diets are short on calcium. I take 1000 milligrams of it daily and keep my fingers crossed. My own mother suffered from rheumatoid arthritis for nearly forty years and was in constant pain. By the end of her life, her limbs had become misshapen, her gait had changed and even the smallest movement required tremendous effort on her part. More than anything else, her radiant personality underwent a radical transformation. This used to disturb me more than anything else. She had stopped smiling or enjoying life and her expression altered beyond recognition as her face started reflecting the pain she was suffering. It was a very disturbing phase for the entire family – we

felt helpless and frustrated at our own inability to ease the situation. I swore to myself that I would safeguard against such an eventuality by taking whatever precautions were needed. My daily stretches are just one way of retaining spine flexibility. I am told that simple yoga asanas that stretch the spine are effective in maintaining mobility. I am conscious of my knees becoming stiffer with age and try to keep them active through regular toe-touching (twice a day for ten minutes each). I also dealt with a frozen shoulder by exercising it thoroughly (simple but regular rotation of the joint helped me a lot) rather than going in for heavy-duty painkillers or physiotherapy at a specialty clinic. *To know and understand your body is key.* Only then can you address the myriad problems that advancing years bring with them. I try my best to be in complete sync with all my body's systems. I listen to every sinew and muscle and pretty much know when something is malfunctioning. You too can train yourself to be in tune with your body. Not only will you reduce medical bills considerably, but you'll also be one step ahead of any ailment.

CHAPTER 8

The Grapevine and the Little Birdies

Time and trouble will tame an advanced woman,
but an advanced old woman is uncontrollable by any earthly force.

– Dorothy L. Sayers

$\mathcal{I}$t is a cliché, but like most clichés, there is a grain of truth in the belief that women are born gossips. We do tend to 'exchange views and information' much more than men. My personal opinion is that men gossip a great deal too, but it's called another name! Since we are stuck with the bad reputation, we must be cautious at all times because gossip has a nasty way of boomeranging.

By sixty, most of us have experienced a fair amount of life, with all its ups and downs. We also have a wealth of useless information about our relatives, friends, foes and casual acquaintances. A wise woman knows exactly what information to file away and what to discard.

I have made gross errors in the past by opening my mouth at the wrong time and causing avoidable hurt, only because I didn't know how to distil the material I was privy to. After many a heartache, heartbreak and minor calamity, I am now slightly closer to the stated objective – minding my own business. As women, we tend to meddle in other people's affairs, offer unsolicited advice and generally assume we are helping. However, the consequences of our actions often backfire and words spontaneously uttered lead to permanent misunderstandings and even break-ups of close relationships (I confess it has happened to me and I greatly regret it).

My position today is one of detachment. I prefer to stay aloof. Not that my appetite for juicy gossip has reduced – far from it! These days when I come across tantalizing bits of idle chatter about someone, I try hard not to pass it on, comment on it or take it too seriously. It can become a dangerous game of one-upmanship with no real victors. I also avoid making unnecessary social calls. For one, I don't have the time. For another, it is these very calls that lead to trouble. I have also made a mental list of gossips to avoid – these are ladies whose full-time occupation seems to revolve around gossip. When they aren't talking on the phone they are either emailing or texting whatever they've heard on the grapevine. These women (and a few such men) are best kept at an arm's length, for even an innocent response can be misconstrued, twisted and used against you.

In hindsight, I often wish I had taped my mouth and plugged my ears. Unfortunately, the nature of my job was such that I couldn't, being the editor of two popular magazines. I was constantly bombarded with 'breaking news' and it became second nature to me to process this news, publish some of it and discard the rest. In the bargain, I fell into the trap of talking too much and to the wrong people. Today, I am more conscious and definitely more discreet! I learned the hard way, but you don't have to.

Gossip is often dismissed as harmless but it is *never* harmless. Ask the victims. People who make gossip the centrepiece of their lives end up being lonely, miserable and condemned by all. Gossip emanates from an idle mind, often described as the devil's workshop, so if there is some lesson to be learned from this, it is to ensure that your mind is never idle. Our bodies may age but our minds don't. If you keep your mind actively engaged in something that comes close to a passion, chances are you will stay young and look young. A vibrant, active, curious mind leads to brightness in the eyes, an alertness of posture and overall energy that radiates positivity.

By sixty you know who you are. That in itself is comforting, leading to peace and acceptance of yourself in totality. Making new friends at this stage is often difficult if not impossible. You are set in your ways and routines. Your tolerance level is pretty low and your bullshit antenna pretty high. Just the thought of the monumental effort involved in reaching out to strangers is daunting and tedious. For example, I can tell you candidly that I am not searching for new friendships; it's hard enough to keep up with old ones. But these days, I find I have become far more receptive and cordial if someone extends a hand of genuine friendship. I don't withdraw instantly as I once did. I am glad I have changed and become more approachable. If and when you do come across someone new and interesting, and you also sense a high level of compatibility developing in the future with that person, it is worth keeping your mind open to a new relationship (if you have the energy for it). A tranquil expression is one of the world's most flattering cosmetics. If you project the calm you feel within, you remove at least a decade from your appearance. The trick is to experience that calm.

So, how does one get to that stage?

1. By leading an industrious life. Keep your mind busy.

2. By keeping dreams alive. Who says you must stop yearning after sixty? The world offers so many wonderful opportunities to senior citizen these days so grab them!

3. By retaining a curious mind. Never stop asking questions and never stop seeking answers.

4. By engaging in some form of physical activity. Just walking briskly everyday, climbing the stairs, touching your toes, swimming, stretching or playing a sport are enough to kick-start your day.

5. By involving yourself in community service. This is the perfect time to give back to society. It gives one immense gratification

to help less privileged people when you are in a position to do so. Give your time to a charity of your choice; it is far more valuable than merely signing a cheque.

Working with people who need your help makes you appreciate God's kindness towards you and your family that much more. Besides, you enrich your own life through interactions with the less fortunate. I find working with children very educative, since I learn so much about love and sharing from them. When I interact with children suffering from cancer, I come back chastened and humbled by their courage and determination. I also come back feeling depressed, but never defeated. Children are great teachers, and the time you spend with them makes you appreciate the gift of life and also its vulnerability.

CHAPTER 9

Life after Work

You have to put off being young
until you can retire.

– Unknown Wise Person

*O*ften, joblessness and sexlessness get interlinked, compounding the abject feelings of hopelessness and worthlessness on all fronts. In these insecure times, losing one's livelihood directly affects the libido, whether in men or women. Retirement woes and the thought that life itself is not worth living leads to severe depression for some. Men seem to get harder hit when the time to walk away from a steady job approaches, while women see retirement a little differently and plan for it in a practical way. Anticipating the long hours stretching ahead of them, they invariably figure out how best to make the most of their time. Enjoying grandchildren was an option earlier, but these days most couples live on their own. Besides, today's granny is no nanny! She may want to spend time with her grandkids, but on her own terms and not as a babysitter. If both grandpa and granny face retirement at about the same time, that's even better. Urban couples soon settle into routines that work for them, without taking on the responsibility of looking after grandkids. This attitude is often dubbed selfish by the next generation, but for now a new pattern is in place that recognizes the rights of senior citizens to invest time in themselves, pursue their passions and enjoy leisure activities after decades of slaving in an office.

In as 'ageist' a society as we currently live in, enforced retirement at fifty-eight or sixty has become an important issue. People are forced to let go of jobs they love and have contributed immensely to, because of archaic management policies that stick to a strict retirement age. As I often hear friends sighing these days, 'We should consider ourselves lucky that we are still working hard and our contribution is valued!' This is so true. My journalist colleagues often have to accept editorial directions from colleagues who are half their age. They may resent the audacity of a twenty-six-year-old asking them to resubmit an article and make it more 'contemporary', but they are also realistic enough to realize that this is their last stop. If they throw in their papers, nobody else is likely to employ them. Unfortunately, the cycle of work life is such. It is better to accept a few home truths and make the necessary adjustments than

to retreat into depression brought on by a feeling of rejection. This is not personal – the world is run by dynamic, young people with fresh ideas (look at Barack Obama, who is often referred to as the most powerful man on earth). Older folks have to move over and create space for the next generation. How else will youth progress up the ladder? If nobody is willing to retire what will educated, qualified, ambitious young people do? Is it fair to expect them to wait for their turn (Prince Charles is a prime example here) and if so, for how long? Given the dynamics at the workplace these days, one often hears the phrase, 'If you haven't made it by thirty, you'll never make it.' This is largely accurate. Professionals peak at thirty, consolidate by forty and are ready for change at fifty. This is New Age careerism, and it is a phenomenon spreading rapidly across the world.

Those who accept the laws of employment in this era are the ones who cope better when being laid off or having retired. There is no place for depression and angst once the marching orders arrive. Exit with grace and your dignity intact. I know it is difficult, but better that than a show of bitterness and frustration. If colleagues have planned a farewell party in your honour, attend it cheerfully and accept whatever ugly gift is given to you. Prepare an appropriate speech (keep it really, really short) and walk away jauntily into the sunset.

The problem arises when you allow rage and frustration to take over. *But why me?* This is undoubtedly a tricky phase in any individual's life. While finances may be strong, health may be weak. Either yours or your partner's retirement blues compound feelings of uselessness. People start blaming themselves, blaming family, and even blaming God! It is natural. Suddenly, you feel old and unwanted. This can demoralize the strongest person and often does. It is times like these when you really need strong family support and understanding.

My suggestion is to not wait for retirement, but to prepare for it at least five years in advance. You know you aren't getting any younger. You know it's coming. Plan it sensibly and in an achievable manner. Before anything else, plan your finances! Having your own money in your senior years, rather, enough money to take care of all your needs is essential for a sense of security and happiness. Do not depend on anybody else to bail you out, not even family members. How you achieve this depends on your life situation but it is important to plan steadily, wisely and well in advance.

1. Is your life insured?

2. Does the interest on your savings cover your basic needs? Which means, can you comfortably pay your daily bills (rent, food and other essentials) without touching the capital?

3. Have you put together an emergency fund to take care of unforeseen calamities like a terminal medical condition, hospitalization, fires, car crashes or the other horrible things life unexpectedly throws up?

4. Are you prepared to scale back on a lifestyle that you can no longer afford or sustain? The mental readiness to make major adjustments in this area is very important to your sense of well-being. A lot of people find it extremely hard to give up on a life they've led for fifty years or more, a life that has given them a sense of comfort. They lose heart when they realize they can no longer take small luxuries for granted. From selling a family car to getting a smaller flat, these are major changes that do cause a great deal of stress and anxiety. I have seen women crumble within a few months of trying to cope with a new, more modest order. Even something as seemingly small and inconsequential as giving up items like expensive fruits hits them hard, and they never quite pull out of that depression. They turn into human calculators, perpetually asking for prices and saying, 'No, no, no . . . that's too expensive. Forget it.' They deprive themselves of the smallest pleasures – no movies, no popcorn, no new chappals or sarees, no restaurants, no 'useless' expenditure. That's so sad and silly! With smarter financial planning (pay an expert to do it for you if you don't possess the skills; in the long run it's well worth the fee) you can live a life of dignity on your own terms. For this to happen, you need to acquaint yourself with basic tools. My darling mother had never stepped into a bank, signed a cheque or taken a single financial decision on

her own. She didn't need to as my father handled it all and handled it exceedingly well. I, on the other hand, began to earn and save money at the early age of seventeen. I understood its value and treated my earnings with respect.

I advise my daughters to follow a disciplined pattern vis-à-vis their money. I tell them to save even if it's a thousand rupees, five hundred rupees or two hundred rupees a month. Don't fritter your money away on some temporary thrill like a crazily priced designer bag. Instead, buy a small piece of jewellery – silver or gold – which has some intrinsic value. My entire collection of old silver has been built up steadily over the years and I am very proud of it. My daughters enjoy wearing some of the pieces themselves, and that makes me even prouder. Have I succeeded in getting them to save? Naaah. Not yet. But they are getting there.

My daughter's friend told me about her mother's practice of buying her a gold coin every Diwali. That young girl is now in her mid-twenties and has over twenty-five gold coins to her name, thanks to her mother's foresight. Another parent I know approached a broker to set up a fund for his three children when they were still awfully young. He had cleverly anticipated the escalating cost of education over time and ensured his kids would receive the best thanks to the fund created for them.

Life after Work

Retirement need not be a scary prospect if your mental attitude to it is realistic and positive. But, if you are unable to come to terms with the thought, I strongly recommend therapy. There's no shame in seeking professional help for something you are unable to do for yourself. Retirement can be gentle and comforting if you listen to your heart, body and mind. By all means live life to the fullest, just don't strain at the leash. Push yourself only to the extent your heart can handle.

At all times, believe that your best is yet to come – and it will!

CHAPTER 10

The Battle with Hurt and Disappointment

Nobody grows old merely by living a number of years.
We grow old by deserting our ideals.
Years may wrinkle the skin,
but to give up enthusiasm wrinkles the soul.

— Samuel Ullman

$\mathcal{M}$ost people start to doubt their self-worth once they hit fifty-five. Especially women who begin to feel useless, unattractive, or worse, unwanted. They hold other people responsible for their state of mind and become exceedingly demanding. This can get awfully trying for family members who are preoccupied with their own immediate concerns. Often the children are married with kids of their own by then. They don't have either the time or the patience to indulge crotchety mums who are constantly cribbing about everything. This is the surest way of turning off family, and yet, so many of us fall into the bottomless pit of self-pity. Of course, women's hormones can be held responsible for those awful mood swings and irrational outbursts, but much beyond the 'hormones-playing-havoc' reason lies a far bigger one – low self-esteem. The truth is most women start to believe that by this time they are well past their sell-by date. Let's face it, looks can and do fade. The body resists reshaping, remoulding, and the mind is restless. Meanwhile, partners (generally husbands) are doing just fine with career goals having been met on schedule. They are in a fairly secure space, money-wise and otherwise. Their paunches and flaccid body parts don't bother them all that much so long as they feel respected by colleagues and admired by female associates. Some may have hobbies that take care of weekends while others enjoy the anticipation of post-retirement leisure. Most revel in the past and congratulate themselves for successes big and small. Men aren't looking for anything more than an uncomplicated middle-age, sans medical emergencies and unwanted stress. They are certainly not interested in the moaning and groaning of unfulfilled wives who crib constantly and have lost interest in most things, including sex. This is exactly the time when women need to take stock of their lives and get their act together. If they don't, they stand to lose out. No matter how loving family members are, they move on eventually, unable to deal with a perpetually angry person.

My suggestions:

1. Look beyond kitchen politics and find something worthwhile

to do with your time. Creating opportunities to get out of the home (especially a claustrophobic, crowded one) for even an hour a day could restore some sanity and balance in life. Merely observing the impersonal bustle of other people's lives often gives one breathing space and a fresh perspective. In earlier times, women would piously head for the nearest place of worship since society sanctioned only this one outing. Today women have no excuse and don't need such alibis either. No matter where you are or who you are, it's imperative to carve out some 'alone time' and escape the confines of home briefly.

2. Employ your powers of touch. It could even be a favourite pet who becomes the object of your undivided attention and affection. So be it. Touch therapy is like no other therapy on earth. Stroking a cat or petting a dog makes us feel kinder and more human. It's good for us, and it's even better for our pets.

3. Reconnect with your sexual self. Use whatever methods you think fit – fantasy, role-playing, erotica – but do not give up on sex, especially if in a relationship where sex is important to your partner.

When I speak to women in the age bracket of forty to fifty-five, I am astonished at the number who confess that they're done with sex forever. They believe they've performed their 'duty' (read

produced children) and are now in a position to say no. This can only mean their sexual history is unsatisfactory and that they are repulsed by the idea of sex with their partner. Well, this is the time to indulge in some candid talk. If sex has been a chore and a bit of a nightmare, you should discuss it with your partner freely. By this time, both of you should be comfortable enough to table sensitive issues without embarrassment. If there are aspects of your sex life that you find displeasing, this is the right time to articulate those reservations. Tell your partner what it is about sex that puts you off, and more importantly, what turns you on. Once you express your feelings unambiguously it will lead to a healthy discourse, and hopefully, intercourse! The biggest inhibiter in this area is lack of communication. Women who are forthright about voicing their sexual thoughts succeed in cementing their relationship with partners in a more respectful way. Go ahead and indulge yourself – talk about sex, take it a step further and talk about your fantasies. Be bold and experimental now that you are in tune with one another. If your sexual appetites do not match, fine-tune the routine so that you are both in sync. Try and spend time together in a stress-free zone. Weekends away from family hassles do work wonders for your sex life. But before any of this, free your mind from the wrong impression that it is not appropriate to harbour sexual desire after menopause. On the contrary, it may work in exactly the opposite way. It's goodbye to contraceptives and hello to sexual innovation and adventure, so go for it! Worldwide studies in the subject of sexuality have established that enjoying a healthy sex life is good for a person's overall well-being – it revitalizes you and helps build immunity. Combining all these factors, one would say enjoying relaxed sex within a loving and steady relationship is the answer to a longer life, and there really is no age limit here other than the one you place on yourself. Get creative. The easiest way to induce a romantic mood for lovemaking is via massage. You don't have to be an expert, just invest in a mat and some fragrant body oil. If you wish to further enhance the experience, try aroma candles in a dimly lit room. Post-menopausal women frequently complain of vaginal dryness leading to the death of sexual desire. It is true that intercourse can become increasingly uncomfortable, even painful at this stage but what are lubricants for? Besides, there are other ways to satisfy one another besides penetration. The key is to make sex pleasurable, not obligatory.

The crisis to look out for is this: what happens to one's sex life if the partner passes away? This is one of our society's many hard-to-resolve issues. I know of men and women (some with teenage children) who lost their mates while they themselves were still reasonably young, and have not turned their backs on sex. Once the grieving period passes and real life kicks in, most of these friends admitted unashamedly that what they missed the most was physical intimacy. So consumed were some of them with their guilt and hang-ups that they were forced to sublimate desire and take an enforced vow of celibacy. Well, this may have been the rule during the last century, but mercifully things have changed. How each individual addresses such needs is a matter of choice, but the needs cannot be ignored for long without repercussions. Therapists suggest masturbation as an honourable alternative. Go ahead if that works for you, but like I keep repeating, there is no substitute for tender lovemaking.

It's time judgemental members of conservative societies respected the decisions of individuals to gratify their own sexual needs in whichever manner they think fit.

CHAPTER 11

Stereotypes and More Stereotypes

Age only matters when one is ageing.
Now that I have arrived at a great age,
I might just as well be twenty.

— Pablo Picasso

$\mathcal{N}$ever allow society to define your self-image.

Too many men and women buckle under pressure and passively conform to society's expectations of what they should look like or how they should behave after a certain age. Rubbish! There are no such rules, and if anybody tries to impose them please feel at liberty to tell the person off.

I try and attend functions that honour senior citizens. I have noticed a welcome change in the flow of events at these functions over time. Earlier they used to be sombre, stiff and boring affairs during which a sad bunch of old fogies would be paraded on stage and given a citation. They'd stare myopically at the audience, take a bow and get marched off to their allotted seats by young, impatient escorts resentfully performing weekend duties. Well, Tina Ambani, the vibrant force behind the Harmony Awards for 'Silvers' (as she prefers to call senior citizens) has mercifully thrown all convention out the window. The last function I went to was anything but dull. Not only had she got her Silvers to participate actively in the two-hour entertainment programme, she'd also encouraged them to show off! There they were performing skits, dancing, singing and thoroughly enjoying themselves. They were treated like stars in their own right and given as much importance as professional performing artistes. There was a sense of exuberance in their effort, which completely broke through the old mould of doddering, decrepit people paraded on stage so that society could display a condescending appreciation for them having reached that unattractive age. Sometimes I catch a glimpse of myself at odd times and wonder: how must strangers respond to this woman over sixty clad in a summer dress with tattoos and colourful reed bangles on her arms, enjoying a glass of wine in a trendy club with the DJ playing house music at ear-splitting levels? It must be a pretty incongruous sight – or maybe not? I love my sarees and will never abandon them, but I do meet several grannies of my age or younger who have discarded severe sarees for jeans, salwar kameez and dresses, and are entirely comfortable in them. More importantly, they are comfortable in their own skin. These are India's global grannies – up with the times, ready to adapt and change, and prepared to take on key challenges that earlier generations did not have to deal with. Today's urban granny may be a working woman with a packed schedule that involves frequent travel and hours spent on laptops, organizing much more than just the Diwali dinner for twenty relatives. In keeping with the changes within society, this granny is comfortable enough to handle most aspects of her busy life using modern tools. Chances are she drives her own car, manages her own finances, handles investments, cooks gourmet dinners, takes off on vacations with friends and acquires new skills that may range from scuba-diving to learning Japanese. Her time is occupied even if she continues to view family responsibilities as her primary ones. Her grandkids actively enjoy her company and like being with granny over weekends, watching movies or even sailing! Grannies on their part have stopped lecturing or quoting from scriptures to the point of annoyance. Today's grannies are 'chilled out', perhaps more so than the stressed-out mums. The stereotype is being banished for good! Thank God.

Of course this does not mean grannies have become indifferent to family. It only means grannies have a life (their own) which is as rich and fulfilling as the one enjoyed by women half their age. Grannies dealing with widowhood were once, not so long ago, banished to the backroom and rarely allowed to participate fully in family functions. Bound by hoary tradition to remain in the shadows, they would voluntarily stay out during weddings and other auspicious occasions, turning up to bless others before hastily retreating. Not so any more. Grannies are an integral part of any celebration.

Widows today are encouraged to wear colour, keep the bindi on their foreheads and participate fully in joyous events. This is a healthy, progressive trend that deserves to be actively encouraged by a society that used to once exclude widows and marginalize them totally. Unfortunately, India's rural realities remain stuck in earlier centuries in which widows were stripped of status and reduced to playing the role of unpaid domestics in large, patriarchal households. A widow's life in India is still a far cry from the more liberated lifestyle accessible to her counterparts in the western world. Indian society would still frown upon a widow dating eligible men. Remarriage would still be the exception rather than the rule. The widow's own family would still feel uncomfortable with her enjoying herself excessively (by their standards, of course). It is changing, but not rapidly enough. I have friends in this predicament who feel terrorized by their own judgemental children. They are allowed to go out in groups, but not on a solo date! It is entirely arbitrary and hypocritical, but that's how it goes. Women who dare to challenge these old rules form a minority, and risk being ostracized by their family and society at large. Afraid to buck the system, especially if they live by themselves, they end up conforming to society's expectations rather than rebelling. Within limited parameters, yes, they do manage to carve out some sort of meaningful existence especially if they are financially independent. This is really the key. I also have other friends living with their sons who are given 'pocket money' even though they have their own resources. Finding themselves emotionally vulnerable and defenseless, they prefer to go along with such bullying tactics rather than assert themselves and ask for what is theirs by right. 'What if my son turns on me? What if my daughter-in-law prevents me from eating with the family? What if the minds of my grandchildren are poisoned against me? Where will I go? What will I do?' Afraid of being isolated, these women end up making compromises every single day, going along with diktats and pleasing everybody. Life is certainly not made any easier by the fears and anxieties generated by thoughts of being thrown out – often from their own homes! Legally they may be protected but in reality they remain at the mercy of their family.

Today, the situation for oppressed women is a little better with helplines and police protection available around the clock. Despite that, most women in difficult situations prefer to remain silent and suffer rather than report acts of cruelty, injustice and oppression.

My simple advice to women in this unfortunate situation is to build on your skills and strengths wherever they lie, and whatever they may be. Use your time well – do not give in to brooding, sulking and feelings of martyrdom. Trust me, society these days has no time for sympathy. The stronger you make yourself, the better your life will

be. Remain productive and positive – I know that's a tall order but if you work on getting there in a conscious manner, it is achievable. Establish your ability to contribute to family welfare on all levels. Place a value on yourself – it will ensure others value you too.

I remember an old aunt widowed in her twenties, stuck with an infant son, who came back to live in her father's home and spent the rest of her long life being seen as a nag and a nuisance. The poor woman, denied an education, denied her youth, descended into an emotional pit from where she would interfere in the lives of family and neighbours. Everyone pitied her lot, but nobody was willing to put up with her. She died a crotchety, lonely woman whose life had been thrown away on negativity. On the other hand, I have a beautiful friend who found her husband dead in the bathroom aged forty-two and was left with sufficient money and two kids to raise. Financial anxiety was not an issue but she was part of an extended family and the option of moving out or moving on was not available. Being a practical person, she decided to give priority to her children's education by setting up a trust fund that would safeguard their interests and provide access to the best schools in India and abroad. Then she hired professionals to advise her on the remaining monies. Her expectations were not unrealistic at all – she simply wanted to maintain the lifestyle she was accustomed to. She knew her own financial planning was inadequate and believed the hefty fee she'd be shelling out to experts would be a good investment. That's exactly how it worked out. When I meet her today, twenty years after she lost her husband, I feel happy to see a well-adjusted lady who understood the value of conserving resources, planning ahead and cutting her coat according to the cloth.

At this stage in one's life, health issues are even more important than financial ones though the two are interlinked. Insurance policies are one way to address these, but I prefer investing in knowledge. Knowing your body and listening to its signals often pre-empts health emergencies. Arming yourself with basic information is essential if you don't want to be taken for a ride by unscrupulous specialists and doctors who exploit your ignorance and anxiety. In these days of instant information thanks to the Internet, it's useful to access as much data as possible when faced with a health condition just to keep yourself in the know. A word of caution here – do not self-medicate as it can be very dangerous. Get to understand your medical problems but *always* consult a trusted doctor for treatment. Most problems at this stage involve the inevitable degenerating process that is part of nature's cycle. Of course your bones are going to creak, your joints may swell and you'll suffer bouts of indigestion, even sleeplessness. These do not require drastic intervention. Sometimes simple yoga, a bit of meditation, basic exercise and a healthy diet do the trick. If the problem is more serious, it is best to leave it to those who know the subject. Diabetes, high blood pressure, low blood pressure and a whole host of ailments can get you down if you let them. What

I recommend is a yearly medical check-up, as comprehensive as you can make it. Once you know the parameters, you can figure out what to ignore and what to give priority to. My own attitude is to give the body a chance to heal first. If it's a problem that cannot be resolved without medication, then definitely take it. Fevers, colds, headaches and so on are routine ailments that don't need to be immediately treated with strong drugs. In India most doctors tend to over-prescribe drugs, particularly antibiotics. Go easy on anything that overwhelms the system. Let a fever run its course, provided you know what the fever is. If it persists, you should go see a doctor who may then advise a blood test. Today's immunity systems are equipped to fight off standard bugs – let them do their job.

Major illnesses fall into a separate category. Do not neglect any alien growth like a lump, a fresh mole or thickening of the skin. Watch out for signs that indicate changes in your familiar systems. Don't hide any of this from family members. (Do not feel hurt if the youngsters around you seem indifferent to your pain because it is simply the way teenagers respond. Believe me, they do care but have strange ways of showing it.) Treat your body with utmost respect, it's the only one you have. If you abuse it, there is no backup!

Allow me to remind you once again that health awareness starts in your teens. You build on your resources the way you construct a home – brick by brick and over time. Tune into your muscles, heartbeat, lung power, bones, organs, skin and every inch of your body. Once you are able to do this, you will be saved many a trip to the dentist and doctor. Good health habits begin at home, so start early with them. Don't ignore your body until it's too late.

CHAPTER 12

Death, Love and Longing

Love many things, for therein lies true strength,
and whosoever loves much performs much, and can accomplish much,
and what is done in love is done well.

— Vincent Van Gogh

*T*his morning, I received a disturbing call from a school friend. It was to convey the sad news that another school friend had passed away. The obituary was in the papers, but the two of us talking about it made me realize that I'd had no knowledge that our deceased friend was ailing. I could barely swallow as Z mentioned details about A's battle with cancer and how quietly she'd slipped away. Suddenly, I was face-to-face with my own mortality.

It is when a school friend dies (A being the first one from our class to go) that one's age comes sharply into focus yet again. While feeling a sense of loss for the person gone, one also starts panicking.

If it could happen to her, it could also happen to me. Even though I'm not given to such morbid preoccupations and prefer to focus on more positive aspects of life, I'm increasingly aware of health risks and physical vulnerabilities. A's death reminded me of how precious our time on earth is, and how fiercely we must guard our health.

Most women of my generation took health for granted and even when faced with serious medical problems ignored the basics. This has as much to do with cultural influences as it does with ignorance. Women give their own health alarmingly low priority. They are so busy looking after the health of their families that they end up neglecting themselves. I'm ashamed to admit that I do not go for regular health check-ups. While I advise my daughters about pap smears and mammographies, I myself ignore the lot. Shunning visits to the doctor when required is not a smart thing to do. Taking health for granted is asking for trouble, yet most women do just that.

Men, on the other hand, are more scrupulous when it comes to monitoring blood pressure and other routine health issues. They are better at filing scans and reports as well as maintaining reliable records about their various medications. I was thinking about this while talking to a gentleman who is slightly older than I am. He pointed to a bandaged big toe and said he'd had an ingrown toenail surgically cut. Well, I have lived with a painful ingrown toenail for years, trying to solve the problem with do-it-yourself procedures that obviously didn't work. He introduced me to his wife (my age) who'd just had both her knees operated and was delighted with her newly acquired mobility. Once again, my thoughts flew to my left knee that sometimes has me grimacing in pain while descending stairs. I mentioned it to the beaming lady who promptly invited her young surgeon over to join our conversation, and nearly set up an appointment for me to go under the knife. I politely declined and fled! This probably has to do with my aversion to surgery of any kind though in my heart of hearts I know the lady meant well. I should be more open to addressing this problem in a sensible way especially since I love travelling and often find myself struggling on escalators, trying to hang on to my hand baggage while maintaining my balance.

For those of us who love the thrills that travel provides, there are a few handy tips I'd like to share.

1. Travel light! This should become your golden rule. Pack only the essentials that will see you through the trip. Most of us unnecessarily pack clothes that we *may* need as backups. My suggestion is to pack smart and stick to a mix and match formula that allows you to change your look with a few clever accessories like a scarf, shawl, belt or jewellery. Women also tend to pack too many shoes and sandals imagining they'll look shabby if they repeat their footwear. Not so. I restrict mine to three pairs – one pair of heels, one pair of comfortable chappals or sandals, and one pair of shoes that can double up

for meetings as well as an evening out.

2. Invest in good, comfortable shoes. Nothing can ruin a holiday or business trip as much as shoe-bites. If you cannot walk without wincing, you are wearing the wrong shoe. Most destinations these days involve a great deal of walking, and most stations and airports also require you to hotfoot it. What's the point in suffering as you trudge along, often carrying a heavy handbag and several shopping bags? With hardly a porter in sight, especially while travelling overseas, you may be required to handle your own bags which is no easy task. Ever tried lugging thirty kilos on and off a conveyor belt? You could sprain your back, damage your wrists or even twist an ankle. You could also end up with a hernia or worse, cardiac arrest. Overexertion is a sure kill joy. If you want to enjoy your trip, be upfront about what your body can and cannot cope with. I have ruined several journeys handling overstuffed bags or walking those inevitable kilometres with corns and calluses on my feet. No stilettos please! Substance wins over style here. Better have a few inches less in height than a broken ankle.

3. Keep your hand luggage as light as possible. Always carry your regular medication in the bag, and always with a small toilet kit in case of delays (do keep in mind security regulations that specify what can and cannot go into this kit – liquids,

creams and perfumes under hundred millilitres are allowed in transparent ziplock bags). An extra pair of spectacles should be packed into the suitcases you plan to check-in, as also copies of any important medical information (such as a rare blood group, a condition that requires specific drugs or allergies that are life threatening). Copies of medical insurance are important as well. Different women have different views on packing precious jewellery in their suitcases. My view is that it's better to wear whatever valuable jewellery you want on your person, and carry just inexpensive baubles which can be packed away. Given the rampant thefts at airports these days, it isn't worth taking the risk of having your jewellery case pinched (yes, it can happen even if you double lock your luggage). The whole idea of travel is to enjoy yourself without the anxiety of losing valuables, and the tension involved in safeguarding precious jewellery is not worth it. As you may be aware, even five-star hotel room safes can be cracked open. I know four young couples holidaying together at a seaside resort who came back to their fancy suites only to discover their safe deposit boxes had been ransacked! Gone were their wedding rings, watches and passports. This sort of an incident is not unheard of, even at the best of places so beware. Better still, leave valuables at home.

4. Assisted travel has still to come of age in India. Ramps cannot

be taken for granted in public places, even though the newer airports are slightly more senior friendly. Most staircases do have support railings, but while travelling it's best to look out for elevators or escalators, even if that means walking a few extra metres. Toilets for those in wheelchairs have become mandatory, but this is still a rarity in India. Given the number of people who require such aid this is highly inconvenient. The rule here remains the same – travel light. Before embarking on a journey, do your homework. In case you are not computer savvy, find someone who is! Visit the websites of hotels before you book them. Make sure the hotel you select is ramped at all levels. Avoid crowded, touristy areas and enquire about public transportation that accommodates wheelchairs. I realized just how crucial these facilities are while travelling through Europe with a relative who needed the extra assistance being temporarily wheelchair-bound after a fall in Rome.

5. Make sure to carry a bottle of mineral water at all times. Most of us don't realize how dehydrated we get on a vacation simply because we forget to drink sufficient water. I also like to keep a packet of my favourite cookies on me, just in case I feel hungry but am not near a conveniently located eating place.

Most hotel rooms these days provide a complimentary tea/coffee station in the room. I like my morning cuppa to be Darjeeling tea,

so I remember to carry my favourite tea bags (this is most handy since I am a late riser and don't have to leave the room to make it for the breakfast service in the hotel). Senior citizens do require a few extra considerations to make their lives more comfortable, and fortunately, the travel industry is now waking up to their specific needs. The grey buck cannot be ignored! It is this segment that has the financial resources to travel, and is doing just that.

ENJOYMENT QUOTIENT

Just as we possess an 'IQ' (or 'intelligence quotient'), we also possess an 'EQ' (not to be confused with 'emotional quotient'). I am referring to the 'enjoyment quotient' that all men and women over sixty are entitled to – they've earned those perks!

The idea of enjoyment may vary as one man's pudding is often another man's poison. It is important not to remain permanently bogged down by worries that vary from broad family issues to more health-related concerns (some may call these 'mini obsessions'). Since energy levels do dip as one gets older, the very thought of seeking enjoyment can generate stress. However, one has to identify what gives pleasure – reading, music, movies, gardening, food, grandchildren, meditation, painting, friends, cooking, golf, cards, clubs, knitting – I could go on and on. Once you know the source of your relaxation, you should consciously make time for it, even chase it. Minus guilt!

Our culture is often judgemental about enjoyment or what it calls 'hedonism'. I am all for an innocent pursuit of the same, provided it does not harm anybody or the self. Some amount of eccentricity is not just allowed at this point in your life, but is mandatory! You are entitled to a little craziness. It adds the much needed zing to an otherwise predictable existence crammed with health and family issues. An occasional drink can be most enjoyable, but daily tippling could get you into trouble. My mantra is simple – everything in moderation.

I would love to undertake a trek to Mansarovar. It is arduous and I am not sure I'll be able to cope. So, do I go into a sulk? No. I comfort myself by reading other people's accounts of their pilgrimages and visualize the beauty of the place. I dream of attending the Mardi Gras festival in Rio. I know I should have planned it twenty years ago but I didn't! Today when I watch clips of the festival on TV I almost feel I'm there dancing the samba with those incredibly costumed dancers.

My father really knew how to enjoy himself right into his nineties, but he was wise enough to recognize his limitations. He loved eating out at new restaurants and kept a close watch on food columns to help him decide which one to try next. Once there, he'd peck at his food and eat such tiny amounts that we'd wonder what his enthusiasm really lay in, since it certainly wasn't the food. He explained that it was the novelty of the experience rather than the quantity of the cuisine on his plate that attracted him. He enjoyed the entire experience right from dressing up to being driven to the restaurant and back. His levels of enthusiasm to try new places used to exhaust us, but now I fully appreciate his tremendous zest for life.

CHAPTER 13

Losing a Partner

When you are sorrowful look again in your heart,
and you shall see that in truth you are weeping
for that which has been your delight.

— Kahlil Gibran

This remains the number one anxiety for most people and it cuts across age. We all live in dread of being left alone, left marooned, left high and dry, left to our own devices or left to somehow cope with life after the loss of a mate.

This is true even for women trapped in far-from-perfect marriages! They'd rather cope with the aggravations generated by a less-than-perfect spouse than have to live by themselves. By sixty, you should be gearing up for such an eventuality in an undramatic, sane way. I know it is a morbid precaution, but it is also necessary to arm yourself against the worst-case scenario – losing a partner.

To begin with, you must assess your financial status. Do so when your partner is still around. Be transparent in these matters and don't worry about whether it looks bad to ask such questions. In an intelligent, trusting marriage such uncomfortable truths are unavoidable and must be addressed. You have the right to know your exact financial status in case your partner dies. How protected are you? Life insurance, health insurance, a certain fixed monthly income that covers your needs plus a cushion to fall back on during emergencies is the basic format. Over and above that, you need to know that you will not be inheriting any debts. This is of utmost importance – there should be a clean and clear picture about finances, and an assurance from your partner (with documentary proof) that frees you from the burden of repaying borrowed money. Next, you need to know about investments – any securities, bonds, shares, property or assets that you may inherit. You also need to know whether a certified will has been created, and if it has, with whom it has been kept. Has it been witnessed? Is it valid? Notarized? If not, it has no legal sanction and could take years to implement with your lawyers making money from the document but none coming your way!

Once you get the full picture of your finances, you can plan your own future expenses and tailor them according to the funds available. There is no point in getting foolishly sentimental at this stage and shying away from asking relevant questions. Too many

people I know have suffered due to their ignorance and hesitation in seeking answers. Your partner should have no problem sharing this information with you either. It's a question of your mental health and overall security. Planning for emergencies at this stage is also a sensible way to cope with unscheduled issues, generally health related, like an unexpected surgery or the unfortunate diagnosis of a terminal illness. How prepared are you to deal with that money-wise and emotion-wise?

Most women postpone thinking such thoughts because they consider them 'inauspicious' but it is crucial to financially plan for such crises so that you aren't caught off guard if something like this occurs. Families have been traumatized and lives turned upside down with emergencies in the form of accidents, disease or even divorce leading to total chaos. Nobody can possibly anticipate everything but if one looks around and takes a practical view of other people's lives, it is comparatively simple to figure out what could go wrong in your own and prepare for it. In broader terms, this is known as 'disaster management'. Every family should create its own manual and inform all their family members about its contents.

I keep detailed notes in a leather-bound diary that record health and financial issues, expenses and other matters that impact the family. I feel it's a constructive way to stay on top of things and provide a handy record to the next generation that could prove to be useful. It is more in the nature of a log book or an informal diary that tracks the major developments in our lives. I lace mine with personal anecdotes, insights and emotions (good and bad). I find it most therapeutic. Also, when you confront issues head on without camouflaging them, it helps you to problem-solve. Once the tricky areas are identified in black and white, there is no running away from them. A small warning: be careful what you commit on paper. My father (a canny law expert) always reminded me not to carelessly leave incriminating papers around. You never know who may find them, and worse, misuse them. If you feel there are references that can get you into trouble at some future date, tear up the papers when their use is over. Ditto for any photographs that are likely to cause embarrassment either to you or your family. Women who hang on to such mementos live to regret the day their precious memories come under assault by those who can exploit them.

CHAPTER 14

The Solo Flight

Language has created the word 'loneliness'
to express the pain of being alone,
and it has created the word 'solitude'
to express the glory of being alone.

— Paul Johannes Tillich

*T*his is perhaps one of the most haunting fears for men and women. It manifests itself around the age of fifty, when the first, hesitant thoughts revolving around one's mortality crowd the brain.

Most women of my mother's generation actively prayed to be the 'first to go' since they were entirely ill-equipped to deal with life after their husbands' death. Being financially and emotionally dependent throughout their lives, women of that era preferred death over an uncertain future. A woman who died a *soubhagyawati* (one who is safe from the curse of widowhood) was deemed blessed by the Gods.

Today the financials may be different but the psychological

burden remains virtually unchanged. With the nuclear family model having overtaken the old extended family system, there are no support groups to cushion impending loneliness – unless the widow or widower decides to take the initiative by reaching out and reorganizing priorities. The very first priority being to assess one's finances clinically. In order to do that, one has to be in a stable, trusting relationship.

How many women know the exact financial position of their husbands (bank account details, investments, assets, debts, liabilities, insurance policies and the existence of a valid will)? There is no shame in seeking out such vital information during the person's lifetime. Asian society deems this inauspicious and even inappropriate but it really is not so. Too many women have found themselves in dire circumstances after the death of their partners. The shock of coping with the tragedy is followed by the even worse shock of uncovering the true state of financial affairs, which may be messy, or worse, fraudulent. Safeguard against this by taking one another into confidence. Share your views on this freely and frankly. If you do not want to make the contents of your will known to your family during your lifetime it is perfectly acceptable, but do let them know that the will exists and inform them as to who has the notarized copies.

Planning for a solo future can be very traumatic and trying but treat it as the topmost priority. Once you sort out the money plan you'll be able to accurately assess the adjustments you may have to make – scale back or scale up!

Once you've sorted out your expenses, pay attention to lifestyle changes. The person you counted on to be there at all times is no longer by your side. Now what? Brooding and lapsing into depression will get you nowhere. Your friends will be around to offer tea and sympathy for sometime but eventually, they'll have to move on too. If you are fortunate, you may get the support you seek from family members but don't bank on it. Ultimately, you have only yourself to lean on. Face that fact first. Once you come to terms with your aloneness (not loneliness), you will be able to rethink your life and priorities in a more manageable way.

Grief spares nobody, remember that. Each and every human being has to deal with sorrow at some level. You aren't the only person in the world feeling sad, even if that's how it may feel at the time. Do not deny grief or run away from it. Grieving helps you to deal with pain. If you suppress it, the pain remains unresolved and can destroy your peace of mind and even your health. Some societies have an official period for grieving, after which people are expected to carry on with their lives and resume normal activities. This has its advantages, but human beings are unique and cannot be programmed to switch on and off their emotions. No third person can decide for you as to how long you need to deal with the loss of a loved one. You will know from within yourself when that searing stab of sorrow is replaced by an abiding sense of loss – the latter emotion is easier to cope with while the former can overwhelm you. Think of it as a new journey, as a solo flight. Think that you have to make the most of the time you have ahead of you. Do not succumb to feelings of guilt about what you can and cannot do, or should be doing. Life has to go on in a constructive, meaningful way.

The sooner you establish a routine for yourself the better. Structuring time imposes its own discipline. Identify what brings you solace (music, books, exercising, trekking, meditation or any other activity you enjoy) and concentrate on maximizing that pleasure. The busier you are, the less time you'll have to brood. I find that those who reach out to other people in the same situation heal much faster through shared emotions and experiences. This is the time to look after your health even more scrupulously. Eat well. It helps keep low spirits at bay. Seek out those who spread positivity in your life – spiritual leaders or even friends who exert a soothing influence. Surround yourself with objects that uplift your inner being. Do not lapse into a morbid preoccupation with your partner's belongings such as clothes, photographs or other personal objects that become daily reminders of your own loss. Honour the person's memory by all means, but do it in a manner that lessens, not enhances, your grief. Letting go is the hardest thing to do, but it is possible if you make a conscious decision to do it. Pack away all that you know will not be required. Give away clothes to those less fortunate. Distribute whatever you can, whatever can't be preserved for posterity. Remember, closure is essential. Say your personal goodbye in a way that has deep meaning for you – it could be via a letter to the dearly beloved who is no more (very cathartic) or it could be a prayer meeting. You could even visit a place (not necessarily a pilgrimage spot) that had special meaning in both your lives and spend time there before coming home to yourself.

No matter at what age you lose a partner, it is still one of life's biggest losses. But you still have years and years ahead of you. Make a two-year plan and adhere to it if you can. This plan has to be reasonably comprehensive, practical and achievable financially plus emotionally. Once you take life two years at a time, it will fall into its own rhythm. In case you are compelled by circumstances to scale back, do with less or even get into your partner's business (unfamiliar territory, perhaps), equip yourself with knowledge first, understand the trade and only then take the plunge. I know quite a few friends who were thrown into this situation and managed to turn their lives around quite dramatically. Today, they are successful business people who have pulled the company together and taken it forward even though they started off at ground zero.

This is also a good time to explore different ways to give back to society by volunteering for any kind of social service that you find inspiring. Without necessarily joining an NGO, you can begin in your own home by educating a house-help's child, teaching neighbourhood kids to appreciate music and dance, reading to those who cannot strain their eyes too much or even acquiring a new skill that can be shared. It is amazing how this sort of reaching out can transform one's life and enrich it in the long run.

CHAPTER 15

The Lightness of Being

When grace is joined with wrinkles,
it is adorable.
There is an unspeakable dawn in happy old age.

— Victor Hugo

Often, I find myself struggling to remember where I'd put my reading glasses last only to discover them on top of my head. I tend to forget what I myself have identified as 'very important' – it could be dates or activities, even objects. I have given up looking for misplaced stuff. It happens.

Most people of a certain age (anyone between forty and ninety!) suffer periodic bouts of memory loss. Nothing too drastic, just stuff that comes under a broad category called 'absentmindedness'. It begins with familiar, day-to-day objects that mysteriously disappear, and progresses to forgetting the names of people one has met just a few days ago. These lapses can be embarrassing but this is a part of the general degenerating process. Other than recognizing it for what it is, the only other option is to keep a small notepad handy and write memos to yourself. I do this a lot, except sometimes I lose the notepad itself! Then, I'm in trouble. Some people rely on Post-it slips which are placed at prominent spots around the house like the door of the refrigerator, inside the front door, on the dashboard of the car, on top of the bathroom mirror, etc. Others put timely reminders into cellphones and laptops, or best of all, brief family members to remind them. I play it safe by adopting any and every method that helps me to perform chores on time. I eat five water-soaked almonds first thing in the morning since someone told me years ago that almonds are good for the brain. Others swear by white pumpkins or fish heads! Whatever works for you. There have been quite a few attempts to commercially market memory drugs. The medical establishment does not endorse most of them and I have never tried any of these artificial memory boosters myself. I remain rather wary of all such products, since I know one simple truth – the brain, like the body, needs regular exercise. The more active you keep it, the better it performs. A lazy brain is like lazy muscle – both get lax and useless if unused. Tautness and alertness of mind and body can be achieved through a daily regimen of exercise that stimulates brain cells and tones up the muscles. There is nothing complicated about these routines. Just as you stretch your limbs, deep breathe and work out those fat cells, do the same with your brain cells. My recommendation? Sing. Try and recall the lyrics of your favourite old songs and sing away. Not only is this enjoyable, but it also helps you jog that memory. Better still, sing and dance together. It's relaxing and fun plus it burns those stubborn calories!

Memory can play games with you like nothing else. It is a strange thing indeed. My father's brain remained youthful, sharp and scarily alert till his last days (he died at age ninety-eight) but even he would occasionally forget the names of his grandchildren or what he'd eaten at breakfast. However, if anybody asked him to recite Abraham Lincoln's speeches or Jawaharlal Nehru's 'Freedom at Midnight' address, he would oblige without forgetting a single word. Ditto with lengthy Shakespearean passages or the poetry of John Keats. Since he worked in the legal world, his vast experience and knowledge of the subject provided him the opportunity to offer free legal aid to countless underprivileged people who flocked to him for advice. He could recall the minutiae of various laws and by-laws without having to refer to the impressive tomes on his bookshelf. This gives me great pride but it also reminds me of his disciplined life and most importantly, his awareness levels. If you are aware of your body in all its aspects, you can pre-empt many problems that occur later in life. I often joke that I listen more keenly to my knees and shoulder joints than to boring politicians or other gasbags! I assure you it works.

Managing anger is next on my to-do list. I confess I have not been able to rein in either a show of impatience or a mini-tantrum. As one grows older, either of two things happen: the fuse gets shorter or you mellow. I have yet to achieve mellow and my fuse is definitely far shorter than is good for health. Small irritants get me the most and it isn't even as if I'm a perfectionist. Sloth, rudeness and inefficiency are my trio of bugbears. I have tried hard to at least camouflage my annoyance when faced with one, or all three, but no luck so far. This is frustrating since all along I've been told awareness of the irritants is the first step, that if a person acknowledges a problem chances are it will get resolved. Well, I have 'acknowledged' my problem a thousand times but it refuses to go away. Talking to friends, I take small comfort in the fact that I'm not alone. Several people suffer the same way, unable to cool down and ashamed of their lack of control. Deep breaths and counting don't do it for me but walking away does. I used to think of this as an act of childishness, as if I was running away from a problem. Today I see it differently. When I can sense an impending argument or an ugly storm, I withdraw instantly! I physically leave the place (this is impossible to do on a flight, however) and wait till my breathing is back to normal. Once I know I can conduct a sane, calm conversation, I get back to the starting point feeling far more in control.

Anger is such a negative emotion. It distorts the face and makes even the most beautiful person look unattractive. The entire personality undergoes a dramatic transformation. Yet, some of us really struggle to battle the demons that make us utter harsh words, shout, abuse, lash out and insult others. I admire those who stay unperturbed and impassive through tumultuous situations. Experts say anger runs in families, so I promptly blame mine on genes. Experts also say it is one of the easiest-to-manage emotions. Once again, the route suggested involves meditation and breathing techniques. I intend to learn both very soon but till such time, let me share a few tips that work for me. I have already revealed one (walking away) so here are a few more.

1. Avoid situations that have landed you in trouble in the past, such as meaningless discussions when either you or the other person is slightly inebriated. Alcohol fuels arguments. Alcohol, consumed even in small amounts loosens tongues and unleashes negativity. I am a wine drinker, but I notice its often confusing effects. Sometimes wine makes me giggly and light-hearted but sometimes I get aggressive and argumentative. Not good. *This never used to happen to me!* I moan and groan after an episode. Someone or the other always reminds me that I was much younger then. So true. It *is* age-related. I laugh when my husband reminds me how we used to pop a bottle of champagne and finish it over dinner. I'd be at my bubbliest and wittiest during those heady evenings but alas, not anymore. Two glasses down I feel unsteady on my feet. If I go for the third, God help me and anybody else in my proximity. Knowing this about my system, I am very careful

not to exceed two glasses of wine these days. Especially if there are irritants around that could act as triggers to my temper.

2. Review your personal anger. What brings it on? Is it rational by other people's standards? Were you justified in losing your temper? Do you regret your words or actions? Write down the sequence of events leading up to the explosion. The process of documenting rage in an analytical way is therapeutic in itself.

3. Distract your mind. Anger can be dissipated easily if you consciously turn your back on it. My anger buster is generally a Bollywood blockbuster. Off I go to the nearest multiplex and emerge calmer a couple of hours later, having treated myself to popcorn and a film. It's a quick fix but it works for me.

4. Express regret if you've hurt someone's feelings, especially if you've done so sans any provocation. Apologize, and mean it. It immediately takes away the nasty, cold edge that fights create.

5. Have a cold shower. It sounds like a cliché but it literally cools you down on every level. Besides, it gives you time to think on your own, review your actions and plan the next move in isolation.

6. Avoid sending text messages or emails when furious. The stupidest way to escalate a tense situation is to bombard someone with lethal text messages. They get you nowhere

plus the other person can then build up a case against *you* based on those impetuous messages.

7. Cook. Sounds absurd, but banging pots and pans in the kitchen is better than banging your head against a wall. Cooking is creative and needs attention. Your mind stays on chopping, mixing and grilling - ingredients, not people. Once your focus shifts to the dish being attempted, your anger gradually vanishes and the fumes from your ears get replaced by the lovely aromas from your wok!

8. Sleep. Most times, fatigue rather than a logical reason leads to fights. A tired mind takes the easiest route when confronted, going into defence or war mode. Most of us these days are compromising on our sleep which leads to various problems like an inability to cope with minor lapses. Our breaths are getting shorter and shorter, with the result that we are allowing ourselves to let fly where in the past we would have been more patient. Catching up on sleep is one of the best remedies to counter anger. Drink a glass of water (dehydration leads to terrible mood swings) and tuck yourself into bed. Don't read and don't watch TV. Command yourself to sleep. An hour's nap can help you to overcome almost anything! It's hard to induce sleep when your heart is pounding but even settling yourself into bed is a good enough antidote to anger.

9. Chant. Those of you who are familiar with Buddhist chants

will know what I mean when I say they touch, soothe and revive your soul. If you know how to chant, do it. Chanting is for troubled souls. It is one of the best ways to deal with emotional turbulence.

Ageing need not be such a scary proposition if you mentally prepare for it, accept it, and even embrace it. Look at Sophia Loren at seventy-five saying cheerfully, 'I am still waiting to grow up!' That's the spirit. Which brings me to the dreaded fear factor – from the age of fifty onwards, people start to shut down their systems. Some switch off altogether while others gradually change gears and slow down mentally, emotionally and physically. This need not be the case! I see women who look stricken when they discover an age spot, for instance. They want to hide. They feel ashamed and angry. They cannot believe their skin is merely saying, 'It's time to take extra care of me. Please use sunblock even if you are planning to stay indoors.' Skin is very, very sensitive and some areas of the skin on a woman's body are more sensitive than others (under the eyes, under the chin, the skin on the neck and around the mouth). Merely moisturizing and cleaning won't do.

I discovered sunblock a bit too late in the day and I really regret my ignorance! I used to imagine sunblock was exclusively used by Australian cricketers. I'd watch their painted faces and feel sorry for the guys. Also, I confused the use of sunblock with tanning. I would wonder why India's Harbhajan Singh was so particular about becoming a few shades darker. That's when I discovered dark, discoloured patches under my eyes. I'd seen a small one years ago and ignored it. These were different – I looked like a raccoon and it wasn't on account of sleeplessness. When I set up an appointment with a skin specialist, I was sure she'd tell me about a faulty diet and bad sleeping habits. Instead, she'd asked me to come back the next day with all the skin products I applied on my face – from moisturizer to foundation. I dutifully packed what she'd asked for and emptied the bag on her desk. She quickly went through the multiple jars and tubes and asked me bluntly, 'These are fine, but where's the sunblock?' I sheepishly confessed I didn't use one, never had. That's when she took me through the whole process of just how damaging the strong rays of the sun were on skin, what with the ozone layer depleting and pollution levels increasing. All that she was saying made perfect sense. So, what was I waiting for? She recommended a 50+ SPF for my skin, which is paper-thin and extra sensitive. She told me I had to have it on at all times regardless of whether I was indoors or outside. 'Even the glare from an open window can damage your skin unless you protect it,' she said sternly. Ever since that meeting three years ago, I have been scrupulously applying a thin layer of strong sunblock all over my face, sometimes reapplying it in the middle of the day as extra insurance. The raccoon eyes took a while to fade, but today those and a couple of age spots are hardly visible.

The reason I'm placing so much emphasis on the physical aspects of growing older is because society judges people by their appearance to a ridiculous extent. People who are unhappy with theirs take that unhappiness and extend it to other areas of their lives.

Men who are particular about the way they present themselves well after retirement are men who show the same level of interest in other areas as well. Compare them to men who equate retirement with freedom from shaving and slouch around the home in pyjamas, their feet shod in bedroom slippers. They end up depressing those around them and eventually lapse into depression themselves. There is no difference between male and female vanity – this is just a myth. Men, even in their seventies and eighties, continue to lead wonderfully vibrant lives provided they take good care of themselves, exercise moderately, eat healthy and live healthy. A brisk daily walk is considered the best exercise but I am not a walker myself. From my balcony, I watch regular walkers as they take their mandatory five rounds of the garden and I envy them! They chat, laugh, exchange notes and generally seem upbeat. On the other hand, I know far younger men in their fifties who refuse to get out of the house for most of the day and behave like they're ready to meet their maker and shake his hand with relief! These men have a negative influence on their families, who feel helpless and even oppressed seeing a once active individual constantly moaning and groaning about growing old. Prostate cancer, cataract, heart conditions, bone breakages – all these afflictions can and do happen. How men deal with it is the issue, though sometimes I wonder whether their worst fears have to do more with balding than anything life threatening. Loss of hair and loss of libido seem to be the primary concerns of the male species. Okay, okay . . . I am half joking, so relax.

I want to share a small story about a woman and a red anthurium. She was someone I'd met briefly and promptly forgotten. When she phoned me to ask about where she could buy a potted anthurium plant, preferably a red one, we got talking. Turned out she lived alone, while her grown-up children lived overseas. She had been a widow for five years and come to terms with her life as a solo player. One of the small pleasures in her lonely existence was her collection of indoor plants. Recently, her favourite red anthurium had stopped flowering and she was afraid the plant would not survive. Could I help her get another one? I sensed she had made the plant an excuse to reach out and talk, so I stayed on the line and asked about her health. That was when she broke down without a warning and told me how desperately alone she felt; alone and abandoned. She told me how the red anthurium brought her instant cheer, especially during grey, dull monsoon mornings. She had begun to equate the colour red with hope, to the extent that when she thought her plant was dying it made her believe her own death was imminent. 'If I say this to my children, they laugh and make fun of me. So I keep quiet and cry.' If I could have, I would have rushed to her home just to give her a hug. Instead, I went on the anthurium hunt – and sent her the plant the next morning. When she phoned to thank me, she sounded cheerful. God knows. On my part I hoped the red anthurium would bloom for long and bring some much needed joy into her solitary life. I'd grandly advised her to count her blessings (she was financially independent and in good health) but even as I uttered those words, I knew that all the comforts in the world cannot compensate for a lack of love and companionship – the two biggest killers of our times.

These days, nearly everyday I meet men and women who seem more comfortable accepting age and ageing than the earlier generations. It has to do with better awareness and greater prosperity, but a lot of credit must be given to changed perceptions in an urban scenario. Age and self-reliance go hand in hand. Once the dependency factor is taken out of the equation, senior citizens and their families are automatically placed on a more level playing field. This is achieved through meticulous financial planning, regardless of the income group. In India, old men and women who were earlier seen as burdens are today viewed as economic assets who can actively contribute to a better lifestyle, either by directly supplementing the domestic kitty or via financial instruments that can aid a grandchild's higher education. Adult children experience less guilt when they realize their parents are not liabilities but dependable support systems who greatly enhance the family's quality of life.

Many individuals I speak to mention a certain 'freedom' that comes with advancing years – freedom to be themselves without any pressure from society or family members. This freedom takes many forms. They are finally masters of their time, for example. They have complete autonomy over money. They feel free to now pursue interests they might have been passionate about in their youth only to abandon them in middle age. They are free to travel, and not just as pilgrims to holy places! They can travel for fun and leisure. They are free to lose weight or put on weight, enjoy an extra paratha or glass of wine, laze till noon or join a yoga class at dawn. All these newly acquired freedoms can be most heady initially. Conditioned to lead a structured existence, senior citizens often turn into creatures of habit, unable or unwilling to deal with change. This is when family and friends can perform a key role by helping them make the transition from a robotic existence to a richer one with greater options.

These days, I watch grandmothers gamely accompanying teenagers to fun events, rock concerts, fashion shows, exotic beach resort weekends and cruise ship vacations. It's a cheerful scene with no apparent generation gap. The grannies are dressed in denims, well-groomed and happy in their skin. So are the granddads! So much for typecasting. A lot of popular TV commercials reflect this social change. Grandparents are no longer projected as wizened old folks on rocking chairs, dispensing boring advice to stone-faced families. Instead, one sees situations where grandparents are an integral part of the fun. This participatory, pro-active portrayal does impact society's mindset in a very positive way. Sometimes when I overhear kids in an elevator teasing grandparents about their 'cool' appearance, I smile to myself. So much has changed in three short decades. Not only is society less cruel towards older people, it is less judgemental too. Hurrah!

A decade of living life gloriously as a fifty-year-old is behind me. Today at sixty-two I have stopped counting! It honestly does not matter how I am seen or even assessed. Often when people find out how old I am I encounter shock and awe. I observe the incredulous expressions on the faces of women half my age and feeling like a kindly aunt start offering instant advice – most of which is listened to respectfully and keenly. Women simply don't want to grow old. Men also don't, but their anxieties are packaged differently. Women over-invest in their physical selves, often neglecting to develop their inner lives at the same pace. By the time they get to seventy, they discover it may be a little late in the day to start worrying over the wrinkles on their souls rather than the ones on their faces. In my experience, men seem far more preoccupied with pension plans and penis performance at seventy. If their finances are secure and they know they can still 'do it' occasionally, they don't agonize all that much over paunches or bald pates. A wealthy man, of course, is free of such preoccupations since he is busy enjoying the assorted freedoms he may have been denied as a young man. He also knows that he can, if he tries, woo a nubile young partner provided he is willing to share his wealth with her. It's an age old phenomenon and not much has changed. Look at an old goat like Silvio Berlusconi in Italy!

In our society, a seventy-year-old lady becomes the world's *ma-ji* (mother); she is revered, looked up to and given a special status. She is seen as someone non-threatening, a benign old lady to be tolerated, provided she doesn't get too demanding or vocal. But you know what, yesterday's *ma-jis* are today's hot grannies who refuse to be marginalized and slotted. They travel, drive, work, play and lead super-busy, super-fun lives. Society, wake up and come to terms with these ladies! Not so surprisingly, travel companies the world over are courting these empowered ladies with especially designed packages that cater to their needs. Beauty parlours and restaurants aren't far behind. There is an explosion taking place across the board and urban senior citizens of both genders are having the time of their lives! With better diets and greater awareness, men and women are not just living longer but living it up. Grey is the new colour of money!

On the eve of my birthday recently, our children watched my husband and me dancing non-stop for over an hour. Sure, my knees hurt and my heartbeat accelerated but the spirit to celebrate and enjoy myself in the company of family and close friends dominated all such hiccups. Later, our son Ranadip commented to the others that he would not have believed such an evening possible. He spoke admiringly about our combined zest for life. I looked around me at all those happy faces and smiled to myself. I reckon a year or so down the line I'll probably be a proud grandma. It is one phase I have been waiting impatiently for. At this point I can't tell you what my report card as a granny will read, but let's just say I'm emotionally geared to nurture my children's children with the same level of love and commitment I have tried to demonstrate towards them over these decades. There are millions of women like me, who no longer run in the opposite direction when the time comes to babysit yet again. On the contrary, it's a mild and reassuring role they actively look forward to. Someone asked me at my birthday party whether I was ready for *vipasana* or other forms of meditation. I answered half glibly and half seriously, 'Not yet. It's too early for that!' What I really meant to convey is that each day of one's life can be converted into meditation. It isn't essential to go off to a distant ashram or cut oneself off from the daily grind in search of intangibles that are supposed to transport you to another, more elevated level. Work is really and truly worship. Ask Asha Bhosle who is busier after seventy-five than she probably was at thirty! There are so many fabulous women not just in India, but the world over, who are demonstrating

the power of sixty. Here's an incomplete list starting with Sonia Gandhi, Hillary Clinton, Sushma Swaraj, Hema Malini, Sharmila Tagore, Meryl Streep, Helen Mirren, Jayalalithaa, Jaya Bachchan . . . add your own favourites.

Each time I put pen to paper (like now!) I am meditating. This is my spiritual charge, this is what keeps me going, what makes me feel vibrantly alive. Fortunately, there is no age bar for my vocation. So long as my brain works, I can continue dancing with words. I see it as God's special gift to me; a divine and beautiful gesture from the almighty that I feel eternally grateful for. Each morning, before getting out of bed, I fold my hands and say a small prayer. It's what my aunt Nimatai taught me. 'Begin your day remembering the divine,' she told me, 'and the rest of the day will go just fine.' How right she was. No matter how stressful, no matter how trying or even painful the next twenty-four hours seem, something melts away with that simple gesture of humility – joined palms in prayer. I feel a sense of strength, of courage, and of hope as I move away from the bed ready to take on whatever awaits me. I like to think of it as the power of love, in a cosmic sense.

When I safely offer advice to close friends tackling turmoil on some front I say, 'Love yourself to start with or else you won't find love for anybody else either. Make your own self happy first before attempting to spread happiness.' People talk of positivity and the energy it unleashes, eventually defeating negative thoughts. There was a time I'd scoff at such clichés and mock those who propagated such quick-fix methods but during the past ten years I have put all that I used to once deride into practice and am happy to inform you, it works! It really does. Not like magic, and definitely not for acquiring frivolous stuff ('Let me send positive vibes towards that gorgeous bag!') but in a quieter, deeper way. You feel better about yourself, you feel far more accepting of life and you believe it's possible to make small things happen. Walking through the streets of Paris with my daughter Arundhati during a bitterly cold winter, I looked at her knuckles turning purple with the icy wind and suggested gloves. Her teeth were chattering (as were mine) when she bravely replied, 'It's more than the cold that's getting to me, but I am coping.' She wanted me to read between the lines and understand her predicament at the time (loneliness in a new city). She could so easily have cribbed, ruining our short time together but she chose not to. I made a thumbs-up sign and whispered, 'Stay positive.' She nodded and smiled, nothing more needed to be said. When I woke up the next morning (it was New Year's Day) in her tiny flat, I saw she'd stuck a few heart-shaped notes on her window pane. One of them read 'Stay Positive'. A simple message that doesn't require extra gyan, but does work when attempted sincerely. When we set out that day her knuckles looked less purple. It definitely works!

Growing old is not an option, but growing old with grace and fortitude is. I have taken an active decision to do just that. People often wonder whether there is some special mantra for making this a reality. Sorry, if it does exist I don't possess it. What inspires me are the uplifting stories I come across, stories that celebrate life at every stage and age. I long to share this exhilaration and joy with others, particularly ladies a decade or more my seniors. It's easy to tell which of them gave up on life without waiting for surprises or even trying to snatch a few wonderful moments. These chronic depressives hang around morosely discussing death, debt and disease, making constant references to their 'autumn years'. They are the ones with mouths turned down and eyes that bear a defeated expression. One can easily tell by looking at them that their exit pass from this magical adventure called life was taken in their forties. There they are, already in the departure lounge, waiting impassively for that flight to their final destination. Then you spot the others, hair carefully coiffed (coloured too), a string of pearls around the neck, coral-tinted lipstick, neatly manicured hands, simple yet elegant attire. Their gait may be slow but there is still a bounce in their walk and a twinkle in their eyes. Their appetite for life and new experiences remains undiminished as they plan their time scrupulously, making the most of every minute. They attend plays and concerts, watch the latest movies, walk in the park, interact with neighbours, keep up with the news, join classes, acquire new skills, new hobbies, new passions – they just don't give up!

Nobody should give up.

If the fear of old age starts haunting you before you hit it, you may as well lie down and wait to meet your maker. If at all there is a message from me to you, it is to take risks. Stretch the imagination. Free yourself from hang-ups. Remember, senior citizenship is about seniority. It is a privilege, not a curse. People will take their cues from you; behave like a martyr or a victim and that's how you'll be treated. Behave like a winner and you are bound to conquer hearts!

- Don't anticipate the worst. Look forward to the best.
- Sixty is the starting line for the last and most exciting stretch of the race.
- Sixty is the time for new beginnings – I swear this is true! If ever you've longed to fulfil buried ambitions and dreams, this is it.
- List out sixty ways to enhance your life the day you turn sixty. The list can include a simple task (a Twitter account – why not?) or something bigger (an art camp in Bhutan!).
- Sixty signals freedom! Freedom from several dull chores you may have been stuck with in your forties – a job you detested or a hobby you'd outgrown. Now is the time to reinvent, so do it.
- Sixty means acceptance, coming to terms with stuff that may have displeased you during your youth – old rivalries, performance anxieties or even a crooked nose. Who cares?
- Sixty can so easily translate into surrender – not to your

fears but to guilty pleasures and secret thrills, like a glass of wine every weekend, lingerie you've longed for and never worn, midday siestas, lazy weekdays, regular massages – just about anything that provides some much-needed personal pleasure.

- Sixty is serious 'me time' – go on, indulge! You can finally afford to get to know yourself all over again. Take time to reconnect with the old you, the essential you – it still exists. Don't feel discouraged if this takes time. After all, you've been another person, played various roles for far too long.

- Sixty and serenity don't always go together. Kick up your heels and have a great time white water rafting if that's what pleases you.

- Sixty is for breaking old rules and making new ones. Tell everybody who tries to put you into a box to go to hell – '*Mujhey Jeenéy Do*' ('Let Me Live') should be your slogan from this point on. Define your own limits and tell critics (family members included) to back off.

- Sixty is a good time to reclaim your life and reorganize priorities. You are the boss and don't you forget that! It's finally you in that driver's seat. Change speed and gears as and when it suits you – no questions asked.

- Sixty is for surprises. Start with surprising yourself! Try things you never thought you could or would. If you wish you'd learnt to play the guitar at twenty, who's stopping you from playing it now? You always dreamt of being a rock star? Your time begins this minute.

Sixty is sexy! Don't laugh. I don't mean in the literal sense (though even in that sense – why on earth not?). Sexy as in being yourself, dressing yourself and just letting go! That, my dears, is the real and only mantra, if at all a mantra is needed.

Forget about looking back. Keep your eyes focused on the future, a rainbow-hued future. Nostalgia is for those who believe there is nothing attractive about the present. That's not you, right? Oh no. Not you at all.

Unlike James Bond, you only live once and that once is now.

Grab life and run.

Simply sixty – how lovely is that? Repeat after me.

Simply sixty. Simply sixty. Simply sixty.

Love it. Live it!

The feasting has just begun . . .